Graphing Calculator Keystroke Guide
and
Drill Exercise Supplement

for

FUNCTIONS AND CHANGE:
A Modeling Alternative
to College Algebra

Preliminary Edition

Bruce Crauder   Benny Evans   Alan Noell

Oklahoma State University

Produced with the aid of the National Science Foundation

HOUGHTON MIFFLIN COMPANY   BOSTON   NEW YORK

Editor-in-Chief: Charles Hartford
Senior Associate Editor: Maureen Ross
Editorial Assistant: Kathy Yoon
Senior Project Editor: Chere Bemelmans
Design Production/Design Coordinator: Carol Merrigan
Senior Manufacturing Coordinator: Marie Barnes
Marketing Manager: Michael Busnach

Printed in the U.S.A.

ISBN: 0-395-93053-7

2 3 4 5 6 7 8 9—PAT—02 01 00 99

Contents

PREFACE

This guide is written as a calculator supplement and drill exercise source for *Functions and Change: A Modeling Alternative to College Algebra* by Bruce Crauder, Benny Evans, and Alan Noell. It is intended to provide basic instruction in the use of graphing calculators as illustrated on the Texas Instruments TI-82 and TI-83. All of the operations necessary for the text are included, and they are presented in the order in which they are needed for the text.

The text *Functions and Change* is a technology-dependent work, and effective calculator use is absolutely essential for success. A concerted effort is made to keep the instructions here basic and straightforward and to make this manual as brief as is practical. This is made easy by the function of the calculator itself, which is designed to provide a maximum of power with a minimum learning curve. As you become familiar with the operation of your calculator, you will find that there are many shortcuts available which are not covered here. Most often we show only what we consider to be the easiest method of producing a desired output from the calculator, but the TI-82 and TI-83 are very flexible instruments which may offer a number of options for getting the same result. You will discover many of these yourself and others by interacting with your colleagues, but you should also look at the extensive manuals which come with the calculator. You may find methods not presented here that you prefer, and you are encouraged to use them.

This guide is organized into three major parts. Part I consists of Quick Reference pages cross-referenced with the *Functions and Change* text. Part II is the Keystroke Guide, which gives graphing calculator instructions. Finally, Part III is an extensive collection of drill exercises for each section of the text, followed by answers. These divisions of this guide are described in more detail below.

In Part I of this guide are the TI-82 Quick Reference pages followed by the TI-83 Quick Reference pages. These pages provide the TI-82 and TI-83 keystrokes for creating tables and graphs, entering expressions, and making the other calculator operations needed in using the text. These Quick Reference pages provide two types of calculator information: instructions for calculator operations and a list of cross-referenced keystoke instructions. The Quick Reference pages are organized section-by-section with the *Functions and Change* text for those sections which require new calculator skills. For each section, succinct instructions are given for the needed calculator operations, followed by a list of explicit keystrokes cross-referenced to the text. These keystrokes are cross-referenced using footnote boxes in the *Functions and Change* text. For example, $\boxed{3.4}$ on page 175 of the text indicates that the exact keystrokes needed to create the graph there are found as item number **3.4**, the fourth such item for Chapter 3, in both the TI-82 and the TI-83 Quick Reference pages (pages 10 and 28, respectively) of this guide. You may find it convenient to select the reference pages that go with your calculator, remove them from this manual, and keep them with your copy of *Functions and Change*.

Part II of this guide is an extensive reference guide to the use of the graphing calculator. This part goes far beyond the keystrokes themselves and carefully details the use of the calculator to perform specific procedures. Not every section of *Functions and Change* involves new graphing calculator procedures, so Part II is not a section-by-section guide, but rather is more general. Three topics are covered in depth: arithmetic operations, making tables and graphs, and the treatment of discrete data, particularly the use of regression to find best-fitting functions.

The final part, Part III, of this guide is a collection of Drill Exercises for each section of *Functions and Change*, followed by brief answers. The exercises are simpler than those in the text. They serve both as practice to develop calculator proficiency and as an aid in fixing key ideas presented in *Functions and Change*. It is important that you work through these, referring to the solutions only if you are unable to complete the exercises without help. The drill exercises are not intended to be challenging, and, if difficulties arise, it is important that you refer back to the appropriate places where the material and keystrokes are explained.

If the manual is to be brief, so should the Preface.

Bruce Crauder, Benny Evans, Alan Noell

1998

Quick Reference Pages for the TI-82

TI-82 QUICK REFERENCE FOR THE PROLOGUE

TI-82 Instructions for the Prologue
Keyboard use

- The blue [2nd] key is used to access special blue symbols on the keyboard face.

- [2nd] [$\sqrt{}$] displays the square root symbol.

- [2nd] [π] displays the special number π.

- [2nd] [ANS] recalls the answer from the previous calculation.

- [2nd] [e^x] 1 gives the special number e.

- [–] denotes subtraction between two numbers while [(–)] denotes a negative sign.

Keystroke cross reference

0.1: 71 [÷] 7 [+] 3 [∧] 2 [×] 5

0.2: 4 [( ] 2 [+] 1 [ )]

0.3: 17 [÷] [( ] 5 [+] 3 [ )]

0.4: [( ] 8 [+] 9 [ )] [÷] [( ] 7 [+] 2 [ )]

0.5: 3 [∧] [( ] 2.7 [×] 1.8 [ )]

0.6: $\boxed{-}$ is used for subtraction as in 9 $\boxed{-}$ 6 while $\boxed{(-)}$ is used to denote a negative number as in $\boxed{(-)}$ 3 .

0.7: $\boxed{(-)}$ 8 $\boxed{-}$ 4

0.8: $\boxed{(}$ 3 $\boxed{-}$ 7 $\boxed{)}$ $\boxed{\div}$ $\boxed{(}$ $\boxed{(-)}$ 2 $\boxed{\times}$ 3 $\boxed{)}$

0.9: 2 $\boxed{\wedge}$ $\boxed{(-)}$ 3

0.10: 2 $\boxed{\wedge}$ $\boxed{-}$ 3 gives a syntax error

0.11: $\boxed{2nd}$ [$\sqrt{}$] $\boxed{(}$ 11.4 $\boxed{-}$ 3.5 $\boxed{)}$ $\boxed{\div}$ 26.5

0.12: $\boxed{(}$ 7 $\boxed{\times}$ 3 $\boxed{\wedge}$ $\boxed{(-)}$ 2 $\boxed{+}$ 1 $\boxed{)}$ $\boxed{\div}$ $\boxed{(}$ 3 $\boxed{-}$ 2 $\boxed{\wedge}$ $\boxed{(-)}$ 3 $\boxed{)}$

0.13: $\boxed{2nd}$ [π]

0.14: $\boxed{\text{ENTER}}$

0.15: $\boxed{2nd}$ [e^x] 1

0.16: $\boxed{2nd}$ [ANS]

0.17: $\boxed{(}$ $\boxed{2nd}$ [$\sqrt{}$] 13 $\boxed{-}$ $\boxed{2nd}$ [$\sqrt{}$] 2 $\boxed{)}$ $\boxed{\wedge}$ 3

0.18: $\boxed{2nd}$ [ANS] $\boxed{+}$ 17 $\boxed{\div}$ $\boxed{(}$ 2 $\boxed{+}$ $\boxed{2nd}$ [π] $\boxed{)}$

0.19: $\boxed{(}$ 3 $\boxed{\wedge}$ $\boxed{2nd}$ [ANS] $\boxed{+}$ 2 $\boxed{\wedge}$ $\boxed{2nd}$ [ANS] $\boxed{)}$ $\boxed{\div}$
$\boxed{(}$ 5 $\boxed{\wedge}$ $\boxed{2nd}$ [ANS] $\boxed{-}$ 4 $\boxed{\wedge}$ $\boxed{2nd}$ [ANS] $\boxed{)}$

0.20: 5000 $\boxed{(}$ 1 $\boxed{+}$ .07 $\boxed{\times}$ 10 $\boxed{)}$
or 5000 $\boxed{\times}$ $\boxed{(}$ 1 $\boxed{+}$ .07 $\boxed{\times}$ 10 $\boxed{)}$

0.21: 5000 $\boxed{\times}$ 1.07 $\boxed{\wedge}$ 10

0.22: 5000 $\boxed{(}$ 1 $\boxed{+}$ $\boxed{2nd}$ [ANS] $\boxed{)}$ $\boxed{\wedge}$ 120

TI-82 QUICK REFERENCE FOR CHAPTER 1

Keystroke cross reference

1.1: $\boxed{(}\ 3\ \boxed{\wedge}\ 2\ \boxed{+}\ 1\ \boxed{)}\ \boxed{\div}\ \boxed{2\mathrm{nd}}\ [\ \sqrt{}\ ]\ 3$

1.2: $1.0067\ \boxed{\wedge}\ 48\ \boxed{-}\ 1$

1.3: $7800\ \boxed{\times}\ .0067\ \boxed{\times}\ 1.0067\ \boxed{\wedge}\ 48\ \boxed{\div}\ \boxed{2\mathrm{nd}}\ [\ \mathrm{ANS}\ ]$

1.4: $1.0058\ \boxed{\wedge}\ 36\ \boxed{-}\ 1$

1.5: $5000\ \boxed{\times}\ .0058\ \boxed{\times}\ 1.0058\ \boxed{\wedge}\ 36\ \boxed{\div}\ \boxed{2\mathrm{nd}}\ [\ \mathrm{ANS}\ ]$

TI-82 QUICK REFERENCE FOR CHAPTER 2

TI-82 Instructions for Section 2.1
How to enter functions

Step 1: Press the $\boxed{Y=}$ key to get to the function screen.

Step 2: Use $\boxed{\mathrm{CLEAR}}$ to delete any unwanted functions that appear.

Step 3: Enter your function using the $\boxed{X,T,\Theta}$ key for the variable.

TI-82 Instructions for Section 2.1
How to make a table of values

Step 1: Enter your function as described above.

Step 2: Press $\boxed{2\mathrm{nd}}$ [TblSet] to get to the TABLE SETUP menu.

Step 3: Set TblMin= to the starting place for the table.

Step 4: Set ΔTbl= to the increment value for the table.

Step 5: Press $\boxed{2\mathrm{nd}}$ [TABLE] to view the table. The arrow keys $\boxed{\triangle}$ and $\boxed{\nabla}$ will let you see more of the table.

Keystroke cross reference

2.1: | Y = | 6.21 | ÷ | (| 0.035 | + | 0.45 | ∧ | X, T, Θ |) |

2.2: | 2nd | [TblSet] TblMin=0 ΔTbl=5

2.3: | Y = | 176 | (| 1 | − | .834 | ∧ | X, T, Θ |) |

2.4: | 2nd | [TblSet] TblMin=0 ΔTbl=5

2.5: | 2nd | [TABLE]

2.6: | ▽ |

2.7: | Y = | X, T, Θ | (| X, T, Θ | − | 1 |) | (| X, T, Θ | − | 2 |) |
| ÷ | 750 | × | (| 5 | ÷ | 6 |) | ∧ | X, T, Θ |

2.8: | 2nd | [TblSet] TblMin=1 ΔTbl=1

2.9: | ▽ |

2.10: | Y = | X, T, Θ | (| 36 | − | X, T, Θ |) |

2.11: | 2nd | [TblSet] TblMin=1 ΔTbl=1

TI-82 Instructions for Section 2.2
How to make graphs

Step 1: Use the | Y = | key to open the function input window.

Step 2: Enter the function using | X, T, Θ | for the variable.

Step 3: Determine an appropriate | WINDOW | setup by using practical information you have about the function. A table of values can be helpful in choosing the vertical span.

Alternative Step 3: For some functions it is appropriate to bypass Step 3 and go directly to the ZStandard view using | ZOOM | 6 .

TI-82 Instructions for Section 2.2
How to adjust graphs and get function values

1. For some graphs it is best to look first at the **ZStandard** viewing screen using `ZOOM` `6` .

2. The `TRACE` key will make the cursor follow the graph, and some function values can be read from the bottom of the screen.

3. To get more precise function values, use `2nd` [`CALC`] and choose **1:value** from the menu. At the **X=** prompt, type in the number you are interested in. Press `ENTER` , and the cursor will move to the point you want and give the function value at the **Y=** prompt.

4. If a graph does not appear in the **ZStandard** screen, try `TRACE`   `ENTER` to find and show the graph.

5. If you want to get a closer look near a point (zoom in), first move the cursor there, and then use `ZOOM` `2` `ENTER` .

6. If you want to see a larger view (zoom out), use `ZOOM` `3` `ENTER` .

7. Manual adjustment of the viewing screen can be made using `WINDOW` . The **Xmin** and **Xmax** values determine the horizontal span of the viewing screen. The **Ymin** and **Ymax** values determine the vertical span of the viewing screen. Proper values for **Ymin** and **Ymax** can often be found by looking at a table of values.

2.12: `Y =`   `X,T,Θ`   `∧` 2 `−` 1

2.13: `GRAPH`

2.14: `ZOOM` and then select **6:ZStandard** from the menu.

Note that the **ZStandard** view can be (and may have been) changed on your calculator.

If **ZStandard** does not show the picture we made, see p. 47 in Part II of this Guide.

2.15: `TRACE`

2.16: `2nd` [`CALC`] Select **1:value** from the menu. At the **Eval X=** prompt, type 3 , then `ENTER` .

2.17: `Y =` 22.75 `X,T,Θ`   `−` 300

2.18: `ZOOM` 6

2.19: `WINDOW` **Xmin**=0 **Xmax**=25 **Ymin**= `(−)` 325 **Ymax**=300

2.20: `GRAPH`

2.21: `2nd` [`CALC`] **1:value** 10 `ENTER`

2.22: $\boxed{Y=}$ 750 $\boxed{\div}$ $\boxed{(}$ 8 $\boxed{X,T,\Theta}$ $\boxed{)}$

2.23: $\boxed{\text{2nd}}$ [TblSet] TblMin=1 ΔTbl=2

2.24: $\boxed{\text{WINDOW}}$ Xmin=1 Xmax=11 Ymin=0 Ymax=100

2.25: $\boxed{\text{GRAPH}}$

2.26: $\boxed{\text{TRACE}}$ $\boxed{\text{2nd}}$ [CALC] 1:value 7 $\boxed{\text{ENTER}}$

2.27: $\boxed{Y=}$ $\boxed{X,T,\Theta}$ $\boxed{\div}$ 40

2.28: $\boxed{\text{WINDOW}}$ Xmin=500 Xmax=1000 Ymin=0 Ymax=30

2.29: $\boxed{Y=}$ 13 $\boxed{\div}$ $\boxed{(}$ .93 $\boxed{\wedge}$ $\boxed{X,T,\Theta}$ $\boxed{+}$ .05 $\boxed{)}$

2.30: $\boxed{Y=}$ Type 260 on the Y$_2$= line. $\boxed{\text{GRAPH}}$

2.31: $\boxed{Y=}$ 235 $\boxed{-}$ 105 $\boxed{\text{2nd}}$ [e^x] $\boxed{(}$ $\boxed{(-)}$ .3 $\boxed{X,T,\Theta}$ $\boxed{)}$

2.32: $\boxed{\text{WINDOW}}$ Xmin=0 Xmax=36 Ymin=100 Ymax=250

2.33: $\boxed{Y=}$ Y$_2$=200 $\boxed{\text{GRAPH}}$

2.34: $\boxed{Y=}$ Y$_3$=235 $\boxed{\text{GRAPH}}$

2.35: $\boxed{Y=}$ Y$_1$= 40 $\boxed{+}$ .29 $\boxed{X,T,\Theta}$ Y$_2$= 50 $\boxed{+}$ .14 $\boxed{X,T,\Theta}$

2.36: $\boxed{\text{WINDOW}}$ Xmin=0 Xmax=100 Ymin=20 Ymax=90

2.37: Not available on the TI-82

TI-82 Instructions for Section 2.4
How to solve an equation of the form *Left Side=Right Side*

Crossing Graphs Method

Step 1: Use $\boxed{Y=}$ to enter *Left Side* on the Y$_1$= line and *Right Side* on the Y$_2$= line.

Step 2: $\boxed{\text{GRAPH}}$ and make necessary adjustments so that the crossing point shows on the graphing screen.

Step 3: Press $\boxed{\text{2nd}}$ [CALC] and select 5:intersect from the menu.

Step 4: Press $\boxed{\text{ENTER}}$ at each of the prompts First curve? and Second curve?.

Step 5: If there is only one crossing point on the screen, press $\boxed{\text{ENTER}}$ at the Guess? prompt. If there is more than one crossing point on the screen, move the cursor near the one you want before pressing $\boxed{\text{ENTER}}$.

Step 6: At the Intersection prompt read the solution from the X= display.

Single Graph Method

Step 1: Write the equation as *Left Side−Right Side*= 0.

Step 2: Use $\boxed{Y=}$ to enter *Left Side−Right Side* as a single function.

Step 3: $\boxed{\text{GRAPH}}$ and make necessary adjustments so that the root is shown.

Step 4: Press $\boxed{\text{2nd}}$ [CALC] and select 2:root from the menu.

Step 5: At the Lower Bound? prompt move the cursor to the left of the root and press $\boxed{\text{ENTER}}$.

Step 6: At the Upper Bound? prompt move the cursor to the right of the root and press $\boxed{\text{ENTER}}$.

Step 7: At the Guess? prompt press $\boxed{\text{ENTER}}$.

Step 8: At the Root prompt read the solution from the X= display.

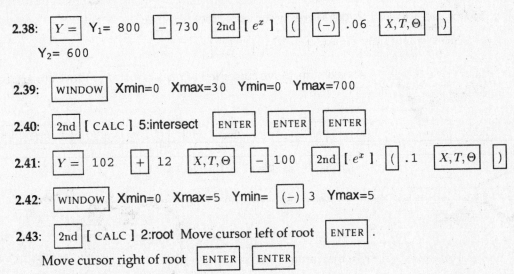

2.38: $\boxed{Y=}$ Y$_1$= 800 $\boxed{-}$ 730 $\boxed{\text{2nd}}$ [e^x] $\boxed{(}$ $\boxed{(-)}$ .06 $\boxed{X,T,\Theta}$ $\boxed{)}$
Y$_2$= 600

2.39: $\boxed{\text{WINDOW}}$ Xmin=0 Xmax=30 Ymin=0 Ymax=700

2.40: $\boxed{\text{2nd}}$ [CALC] 5:intersect $\boxed{\text{ENTER}}$ $\boxed{\text{ENTER}}$ $\boxed{\text{ENTER}}$

2.41: $\boxed{Y=}$ 102 $\boxed{+}$ 12 $\boxed{X,T,\Theta}$ $\boxed{-}$ 100 $\boxed{\text{2nd}}$ [e^x] $\boxed{(}$ .1 $\boxed{X,T,\Theta}$ $\boxed{)}$

2.42: $\boxed{\text{WINDOW}}$ Xmin=0 Xmax=5 Ymin= $\boxed{(-)}$ 3 Ymax=5

2.43: $\boxed{\text{2nd}}$ [CALC] 2:root Move cursor left of root $\boxed{\text{ENTER}}$.
Move cursor right of root $\boxed{\text{ENTER}}$ $\boxed{\text{ENTER}}$

2.44: $\boxed{Y=}$ $Y_1 = 6.21$ $\boxed{\div}$ $\boxed{(}$ .035 $\boxed{+}$ .45 $\boxed{\wedge}$ $\boxed{X,T,\Theta}$ $\boxed{)}$

2.45: $\boxed{Y=}$ $Y_2 = 85$

2.46: $\boxed{\text{2nd}}$ [CALC] 5:intersect $\boxed{\text{ENTER}}$ $\boxed{\text{ENTER}}$ $\boxed{\text{ENTER}}$

2.47: $\boxed{Y=}$ 62.4 $\boxed{\text{2nd}}$ [π] $\boxed{X,T,\Theta}$ $\boxed{\wedge}$ 2 $\boxed{(}$ 2 $\boxed{-}$ $\boxed{X,T,\Theta}$ $\boxed{\div}$ 3 $\boxed{)}$ $\boxed{-}$ 436

2.48: $\boxed{\text{2nd}}$ [CALC] 2:root Move cursor left of root $\boxed{\text{ENTER}}$
Move cursor right of root $\boxed{\text{ENTER}}$ $\boxed{\text{ENTER}}$

TI-82 Instructions for Section 2.5
How to locate maxima and minima on a graph

First graph the function and adjust the window as necessary so that the maxima and minima are clearly shown. Once this is done proceed as follows.

Step 1: Press $\boxed{\text{2nd}}$ [CALC] and select 3:minimum or 4:maximum from the menu.

Step 2: At the Lower Bound? prompt move the cursor to the left of the maximum or minimum and then press $\boxed{\text{ENTER}}$.

Step 3: At the Upper Bound? prompt move the cursor to the right of the maximum or minimum and then press $\boxed{\text{ENTER}}$.

Step 4: At the Guess? prompt press $\boxed{\text{ENTER}}$.

Step 5: At the Minimum or Maximum prompt read the location of the maximum or minimum from the bottom of the display.

2.49: $\boxed{Y=}$ $\boxed{X,T,\Theta}$ $\boxed{-}$ 32 $\boxed{(}$ $\boxed{X,T,\Theta}$ $\boxed{\div}$ 250 $\boxed{)}$ $\boxed{\wedge}$ 2

2.50: $\boxed{\text{2nd}}$ [TblSet] TblMin=0 ΔTbl=500 $\boxed{\text{2nd}}$ [TABLE]

2.51: $\boxed{\text{2nd}}$ [CALC] 2:root Move cursor left of root $\boxed{\text{ENTER}}$.
Move cursor right of root $\boxed{\text{ENTER}}$ $\boxed{\text{ENTER}}$

2.52: $\boxed{\text{2nd}}$ [CALC] 4:maximum Move cursor left of peak $\boxed{\text{ENTER}}$. Move cursor right of peak $\boxed{\text{ENTER}}$ $\boxed{\text{ENTER}}$.

2.53: $\boxed{Y=}$ 32 $\boxed{X,T,\Theta}$ $\boxed{\wedge}$ $\boxed{(-)}$ 2 $\boxed{\text{2nd}}$ [e^x] $\boxed{(}$ 10 $\boxed{-}$ 32 $\boxed{X,T,\Theta}$ $\boxed{\wedge}$ $\boxed{(-)}$ 1 $\boxed{)}$

2.54: $\boxed{\text{2nd}}$ [TblSet] TblMin=0 ΔTbl=10 $\boxed{\text{2nd}}$ [TABLE]

2.55: $\boxed{\text{WINDOW}}$ Xmin=0 Xmax=60 Ymin=0 Ymax=500

2.56: $\boxed{\text{2nd}}$ [CALC] 4:maximum Move cursor left of maximum $\boxed{\text{ENTER}}$.
Move cursor right of maximum $\boxed{\text{ENTER}}$ $\boxed{\text{ENTER}}$.

2.57: $\boxed{Y=}$ Y₂= $\boxed{\text{2nd}}$ [e^x] $\boxed{(}$ 10 $\boxed{-}$ 32 $\boxed{X,T,\Theta}$ $\boxed{\wedge}$ $\boxed{(-)}$ 1 $\boxed{)}$

2.58: $\boxed{Y=}$ Put the cursor on the = sign on the Y₁ line and press $\boxed{\text{ENTER}}$.

2.59: $\boxed{Y=}$ Highlight = on Y₁ line and press $\boxed{\text{ENTER}}$.
Highlight = on Y₂ line and press $\boxed{\text{ENTER}}$.

2.60: $\boxed{\text{WINDOW}}$ **Xmin=** $\boxed{(-)}$ 3750 **Xmax=6250** **Ymin=** $\boxed{(-)}$ 1150 **Ymax=1650**

2.61: $\boxed{Y=}$ $\boxed{(}$ $\boxed{X,T,\Theta}$ $\boxed{\div}$ 4 $\boxed{)}$ $\boxed{\wedge}$ 2 $\boxed{+}$ $\boxed{(}$ 100 $\boxed{-}$ $\boxed{X,T,\Theta}$ $\boxed{)}$ $\boxed{\wedge}$ 2 $\boxed{\div}$ $\boxed{(}$ 4 $\boxed{\text{2nd}}$ [π] $\boxed{)}$

2.62: $\boxed{\text{2nd}}$ [CALC] **3:minimum** Move cursor left of minimum $\boxed{\text{ENTER}}$.
Move cursor right of minimum $\boxed{\text{ENTER}}$ $\boxed{\text{ENTER}}$.

TI-82 QUICK REFERENCE FOR CHAPTER 3

Keystroke cross reference

3.1: $\boxed{Y=}$ 32 $\boxed{X,T,\Theta}$ $\boxed{-}$ 192

TI-82 Instructions for Section 3.3
How to set up statistical plots

Step 1: Press $\boxed{\text{2nd}}$ [STAT PLOT] .

Step 2: Select 1:Plot 1 from the menu.

Step 3: Use the arrow keys to highlight On and press $\boxed{\text{ENTER}}$.

Step 4: Check the other lines in this menu to see that they are correct. Usually you will want Xlist set to L1, indicating that the L1 column goes on the horizontal axis, and Ylist set to L2, indicating that the L2 list goes on the vertical axis.

Note: You do not have to turn on statistical plots each time you want to graph data. This setting remains in effect until you specifically turn it Off. To do so, proceed as above, but in Step 3, highlight Off.

TI-82 Instructions for Section 3.3
How to enter data

Step 1: Press [STAT] .

Step 2: Select 1:Edit from the menu.

Step 3: If it is necessary to clear old data, highlight L1 and then press [CLEAR] [ENTER] . Repeat this for each column as necessary.

Step 4: Locate the cursor in the column where you want to enter data and type each data entry followed by either [ENTER] or [∇] .

TI-82 Instructions for Section 3.3
How to plot data points

Step 1: Be sure that statistical plotting is turned on and the Plot 1 screen properly configured as described above. Also you should use [Y =] to check if old functions are stored and if necessary [CLEAR] them.

Step 2: Enter your data points as described above. In the statistical plot setup outlined above, the L1 column corresponds to the horizontal axis, and the L2 column corresponds to the vertical axis.

Step 3: When data is properly entered use [ZOOM] 9 to display automatically all data points on the screen.

3.2: [STAT] 1:Edit Enter values for d in L1 column. Enter values for N in L2 column.

3.3: Turn statistical plots on using [2nd] [STAT PLOT] 1:Plot1 Highlight On [ENTER] . Set Xlist: to L1, and set Ylist: to L2. (You only need to do this the first time you plot. Statistical plotting will remain on until you turn it off.) [ZOOM] 9 to make the graph.

3.4: [Y =] 462 [X,T,Θ] [+] 28321 [GRAPH]

3.5: [STAT] 1:Edit Enter data for m in L1 column and data for F in L2 column.

3.6: Be sure statistical plotting is turned on and that the function list is clear. Now [ZOOM] 9

3.7: [Y =] 5 [X,T,Θ]

3.8: [GRAPH]

TI-82 Instructions for Section 3.4
How to get a regression line

Step 1: Be sure your data points are properly entered in the L1 and L2 lists.

Step 2: Press [STAT] and use [▷] to highlight **CALC**.

Step 3: Select 5:LinReg(ax+b) from the menu and press [ENTER].

Step 4: You will see a screen that gives the equation of the regression line $y = ax + b$ and values for a and b. The given a value is the slope, and the given b value is the vertical intercept.

3.9: [STAT] 1:Edit Enter t data in L1. Enter E data in L2.

(To make the graph, be sure [2nd] [STAT PLOT] Plot1 is properly configured and [ZOOM] 9 .)

3.10: With the data entered, press [STAT] . Move the highlight at the top of the screen to **CALC**. Select 5:LinReg(ax+b). Press [ENTER] when returned to the calculation screen.

3.11: [Y =] 1.21 [X,T,Θ] [+] 27.46 [GRAPH]

3.12: [STAT] 1:Edit Enter t values in L1 column and M values in the L2 column.

3.13: Use [Y =] and be sure the function list is [CLEAR] . Use [2nd] [STAT PLOT] and be sure Plot1 is **On** and that Xlist: is set to L1 and that Ylist: is set to L2. [ZOOM] 9

3.14: [STAT] CALC 5:LinReg(ax+b) [ENTER] .

3.15: [Y =] 12.89 [X,T,Θ] [+] 252.62 [GRAPH]

3.16: [Y =] Y$_1$= [(] 900 [−] 28 [X,T,Θ] [)] [÷] 32

Y$_2$= 3 [X,T,Θ]

3.17: [WINDOW] Xmin=0 Xmax=30 Ymin=0 Ymax=30

3.18: If you get extra dots on the screen, you may need to turn statistical plotting off using [2nd] [STAT PLOT] 4:PlotsOff [ENTER] .

3.19: [2nd] [CALC] 5:intersect [ENTER] [ENTER] [ENTER]

3.20: [Y =] Y$_1$= [(] 56 [−] 12 [X,T,Θ] [)] [÷] .5

Y$_2$=4 [X,T,Θ]

3.21: [WINDOW] Xmin=0 Xmax=5 Ymin=0 Ymax=20

3.22: [2nd] [CALC] 5:intersect [ENTER] [ENTER] [ENTER]

TI-82 QUICK REFERENCE FOR CHAPTER 4

Keystroke cross reference

4.1: | WINDOW | Xmin=0 Xmax=5 Ymin=0 Ymax=100000

4.2: | WINDOW | Xmin=0 Xmax=5 Ymin=0 Ymax=3500

4.3: | 2nd | [CALC] 5:intersect | ENTER | | ENTER | | ENTER |

4.4: | Y = | Y_1= 64 | − | 64 | × | .71 | ∧ | | X,T,Θ | Y_2= 57

4.5: | 2nd | [CALC] 5:intersect | ENTER | | ENTER | | ENTER |

4.6: | Y = | Y_1= 6 | + | 69 | × | .96 | ∧ | | X,T,Θ | Y_2= 32

4.7: | 2nd | [CALC] 5:intersect | ENTER | | ENTER | | ENTER |

4.8: | STAT | 1:Edit Enter x values in L1 column and y values in L2 column.

4.9: | 2nd | [STAT PLOT] and be sure Plot1 is On. Then | ZOOM | 9 .

4.10: | STAT | 1:Edit Highlight L3 | 2nd | [e^x] | 2nd | [L2] | ENTER | .

4.11: | 2nd | [STAT PLOT] 1:Plot1 Change Ylist to L3, then | ZOOM | 9 .

4.12: | LN | 7

4.13: | STAT | 1:Edit Highlight L2 | LN | | 2nd | [L3] | ENTER | .

4.14: | STAT | 1:Edit Enter time in L1 column and population in L3 column.

4.15: | 2nd | [STAT PLOT] Set Plot1 to On. Set Xlist to L1 and Ylist to L3. | ZOOM | 9 .

4.16: | STAT | 1:Edit Highlight L2 and | LN | | 2nd | [L3] | ENTER | .

4.17: | 2nd | [STAT PLOT] Plot1 change Ylist to L2. | ZOOM | 9

4.18: | STAT | CALC 5:LinReg(ax+b) | ENTER |

4.19: | Y = | .0294 | X,T,Θ | + | 1.6747 | GRAPH |

4.20: | 2nd | [STAT PLOT] Plot1 Change Ylist to L3. | Y = |
5.3372 | × | 1.0298 | ∧ | | X,T,Θ | . Then | ZOOM | 9 .

4.21: | STAT | 1:Edit Enter t data in L1 column and C data in L3 column.

4.22: (You may need to use $\boxed{Y=}$ and $\boxed{\text{CLEAR}}$ out old functions.) $\boxed{\text{2nd}}$ [STAT PLOT] Plot1 Set Ylist to L3. $\boxed{\text{ZOOM}}$ 9

4.23: $\boxed{\text{STAT}}$ 1:Edit Highlight L2. $\boxed{\text{LN}}$ $\boxed{\text{2nd}}$ [L3] $\boxed{\text{ENTER}}$

4.24: $\boxed{Y=}$ .095 $\boxed{X,T,\Theta}$ $\boxed{-}$ .351 $\boxed{\text{GRAPH}}$

4.25: $\boxed{\text{2nd}}$ [STAT PLOT] Plot1 Set Ylist to L3. $\boxed{Y=}$ .704 $\boxed{\times}$ 1.1 $\boxed{\wedge}$ $\boxed{X,T,\Theta}$ $\boxed{\text{ZOOM}}$ 9

4.26: $\boxed{\text{STAT}}$ 1:Edit Enter t data in L1 column and B data in L3 column.

4.27: $\boxed{\text{STAT}}$ 1:Edit Highlight L2. $\boxed{\text{LN}}$ $\boxed{\text{2nd}}$ [L3] $\boxed{\text{ENTER}}$

4.28: $\boxed{\text{2nd}}$ [TblSet] TblMin=1 ΔTbl=1

4.29: $\boxed{\text{2nd}}$ [TblSet] TblMin=215 ΔTbl=50

TI-82 QUICK REFERENCE FOR CHAPTER 5

Keystroke cross reference

5.1: $\boxed{Y=}$ 16 $\boxed{X,T,\Theta}$ $\boxed{\wedge}$ 2

5.2: $\boxed{\text{WINDOW}}$ Xmin=0 Xmax=5 Ymin=0 Ymax=100

5.3: $\boxed{\text{2nd}}$ [CALC] 5:intersect $\boxed{\text{ENTER}}$ $\boxed{\text{ENTER}}$ $\boxed{\text{ENTER}}$

5.4: $\boxed{Y=}$ 21.83 $\boxed{X,T,\Theta}$ $\boxed{\wedge}$ 0.18

5.5: $\boxed{Y=}$ (on Y_1 line) 5.34 $\boxed{\times}$ 1.03 $\boxed{\wedge}$ $\boxed{X,T,\Theta}$
(on Y_2 line) 0.04 $\boxed{X,T,\Theta}$ $\boxed{\wedge}$ 1.5 $\boxed{+}$ 5.34

5.6: $\boxed{\text{2nd}}$ [TblSet] TblMin=0 ΔTbl=5

5.7: $\boxed{\text{STAT}}$ 1:Edit Enter x data in L3 column. Highlight L4 and then 3 $\boxed{\text{2nd}}$ [L3] $\boxed{\wedge}$ 2

5.8: Highlight L1 $\boxed{\text{LN}}$ $\boxed{\text{2nd}}$ [L3]

5.9: Highlight L2 $\boxed{\text{LN}}$ $\boxed{\text{2nd}}$ [L4]

5.10: $\boxed{\text{2nd}}$ [STAT PLOT] 1:Plot1 On. Set Xlist: to L1 and Ylist: to L2. $\boxed{\text{ZOOM}}$ 9

5.11: $\boxed{\text{STAT}}$ CALC 5:LinReg(ax+b) $\boxed{\text{ENTER}}$

TI-82 Instructions for Section 5.2
How to fit power functions to data

The procedure is similar to the one used for exponential regression, except we take the logarithm of the variable values in addition to the function values.

Step 1: Press ⬚STAT , select 1:Edit, and ⬚CLEAR out old lists as necessary. In the L3 column enter the values for the variable, and in the L4 column enter the corresponding values for the function. Now highlight L1 and type ⬚LN ⬚2nd [L3] and then ⬚ENTER . Then highlight L2 and type ⬚LN ⬚2nd [L4] and then ⬚ENTER .

Step 2: To plot the data on a logarithmic scale, press ⬚2nd [STAT PLOT] and select 1:Plot 1 from the menu. Highlight On and press ⬚ENTER . Make sure that Xlist is set to L1 and Ylist is set to L2. Use ⬚Y = and ⬚CLEAR old functions if necessary, then ⬚ZOOM 9 .

Step 3: Perform linear regression as usual: Press ⬚STAT and use ⬚▷ to move the highlight at the top of the screen to CALC. Select 5:LinReg(ax+b), then press ⬚ENTER .

5.12: ⬚STAT 1:Edit and enter data

5.13: Highlight L1 and ⬚LN ⬚2nd [L3] ⬚ENTER . Highlight L2 and ⬚LN ⬚2nd [L4] ⬚ENTER .

5.14: ⬚2nd [STAT PLOT] 1:Plot 1 On. Set Xlist: to L1 and Ylist: to L2. ⬚ZOOM 9

5.15: ⬚STAT CALC 5:LinReg(ax+b) ⬚ENTER .

5.16: ⬚2nd [STAT PLOT] and set Xlist: to L3 and Ylist: to L4. ⬚Y = and enter 4 . 18 ⬚X, T, Θ ⬚∧ 3 Then ⬚ZOOM 9 .

5.17: ⬚STAT 1:Edit enter D values in L3 and P values in L4.

5.18: Highlight L1 ⬚LN ⬚2nd [L3] . Highlight L2 ⬚LN ⬚2nd [L4]

5.19: ⬚STAT 1:Edit and enter data for L in L3 column

5.20: ⬚STAT 1:Edit and enter data for T in L4 column

5.21: Highlight L1. ⬚LN ⬚2nd [L3]

5.22: Highlight L2. ⬚LN ⬚2nd [L4]

5.23: ⬚2nd [STAT PLOT] Set Xlist: to L1 and Ylist: to L2 ⬚ZOOM 9

5.24: ⬚STAT CALC 5:LinReg(ax+b) ⬚ENTER .

5.25: Highlight L1 $\boxed{\text{LOG}}$ $\boxed{\text{2nd}}$ [L3] . Highlight L2 $\boxed{\text{LOG}}$ $\boxed{\text{2nd}}$ [L4] .

5.26: $\boxed{Y=}$ $\boxed{\text{SIN}}$ $\boxed{X,T,\Theta}$.

5.27: $\boxed{\text{MODE}}$ Degree $\boxed{\text{ENTER}}$

5.28: $\boxed{Y=}$ $\boxed{\text{COS}}$ $\boxed{X,T,\Theta}$

5.29: $\boxed{Y=}$ $\boxed{\text{TAN}}$ $\boxed{X,T,\Theta}$

TI-82 QUICK REFERENCE FOR CHAPTER 6

Keystroke cross reference

6.1: (Be sure $\boxed{\text{2nd}}$ [STAT PLOT] **Plot1 is set to Off.**) $\boxed{Y=}$ 30 $\boxed{+}$ 18 $\boxed{X,T,\Theta}$ $\boxed{-}$ 16 $\boxed{X,T,\Theta}$ $\boxed{\wedge}$ 2 . $\boxed{\text{WINDOW}}$ Xmin=0 Xmax=5 Ymin=0 Ymax=50 $\boxed{\text{GRAPH}}$.

6.2: $\boxed{\text{2nd}}$ [CALC] 2:root Move cursor left of root $\boxed{\text{ENTER}}$. Move cursor right of root $\boxed{\text{ENTER}}$ $\boxed{\text{ENTER}}$.

6.3: $\boxed{\text{2nd}}$ [CALC] 4:maximum Move cursor left of maximum $\boxed{\text{ENTER}}$. Move cursor right of maximum $\boxed{\text{ENTER}}$ $\boxed{\text{ENTER}}$.

6.4: $\boxed{Y=}$ Y$_1$=72 $\boxed{+}$ 118 $\boxed{\text{2nd}}$ [e^x] $\boxed{(}$ $\boxed{(-)}$ .06 $\boxed{X,T,\Theta}$ $\boxed{)}$
Y$_2$= 130

6.5: $\boxed{\text{2nd}}$ [CALC] 5:intersect $\boxed{\text{ENTER}}$ $\boxed{\text{ENTER}}$ $\boxed{\text{ENTER}}$

6.6: $\boxed{Y=}$ .338 $\boxed{X,T,\Theta}$ $\boxed{(}$ 1 $\boxed{-}$ $\boxed{X,T,\Theta}$ $\boxed{\div}$ 2.4 $\boxed{)}$

6.7: $\boxed{\text{2nd}}$ [CALC] 2:root
Move cursor left of root $\boxed{\text{ENTER}}$. Move cursor right of root $\boxed{\text{ENTER}}$ $\boxed{\text{ENTER}}$.

6.8: $\boxed{Y=}$ 32 $\boxed{-}$ .1818 $\boxed{X,T,\Theta}$

6.9: $\boxed{\text{WINDOW}}$ Xmin=0 Xmax=250 Ymin= $\boxed{(-)}$ 20 Ymax=35

TI-82 Instructions for Section 6.5
How to find rates of change for functions given by formulas

Step 1: Graph the function and make sure the desired point shows on the graphing screen.

Step 2: Use [2nd] [CALC] and choose 6:dy/dx . Move the cursor as near the desired point as possible, then press [ENTER] .

6.10: [Y =] 16 [X,T,Θ] [∧] 2 [WINDOW] Xmin=0 Xmax=5 Ymin=0 Ymax=300 [GRAPH]

6.11: [2nd] [CALC] 6:dy/dx move cursor to X=2.5 [ENTER]

6.12: [Y =] [X,T,Θ] [−] 32 [(] [X,T,Θ] [÷] 300 [)] [∧] 2

6.13: [2nd] [CALC] 1:value 734 [ENTER]

6.14: [2nd] [CALC] 6:dy/dx Move cursor as near 734 as possible. [ENTER]

TI-82 QUICK REFERENCE FOR CHAPTER 7

Keystroke cross reference

7.1: [STAT] 1:Edit and [CLEAR] out old lists as necessary. Enter t values in the L1 column and N values in the L3 column. Highlight L2 and type [LN] [2nd] [L3] [ENTER] .

7.2: Set Plot1 to On and [ZOOM] 9 .

7.3: [STAT] CALC 5:LinReg(ax+b) [ENTER]

7.4: [STAT] 1:Edit and [CLEAR] out old lists as necessary. Enter N values in the L1 column and values of $\frac{1}{N}\frac{dN}{dt}$ in the L2 column. Set Plot1 to On and [ZOOM] 9 .

7.5: [STAT] CALC 5:LinReg(ax+b) [ENTER]

TI-82 Instructions for Section 7.3

How to generate survivorship curves

The procedure is similar to the one used for plotting with exponential regression. The two differences are the use of the common logarithm instead of the natural logarithm, and connecting the data points with line segments.

Step 1: Press $\boxed{\text{STAT}}$, select 1:Edit, and $\boxed{\text{CLEAR}}$ out old lists as necessary. In the L1 column enter the x values from the life table, and in the L3 column enter the corresponding l_x values. Now highlight L2 and type $\boxed{\text{LOG}}$ $\boxed{\text{2nd}}$ [L3] and then $\boxed{\text{ENTER}}$.

Step 2: Press $\boxed{\text{2nd}}$ [STAT PLOT] and select 1:Plot 1 from the menu. Highlight On and press $\boxed{\text{ENTER}}$. To connect the data points on the graph, from the Type: list select the second type of plot (connected icon). Make sure that Xlist is set to L1 and Ylist is set to L2.

Step 3: Use $\boxed{Y =}$ and $\boxed{\text{CLEAR}}$ old functions if necessary, then $\boxed{\text{ZOOM}}$ 9 .

Quick Reference Pages for the TI-83

TI-83 QUICK REFERENCE FOR THE PROLOGUE

TI-83 Instructions for the Prologue
Keyboard use

- The gold ⬚2nd⬚ key is used to access special gold symbols on the keyboard face.

- ⬚2nd⬚ [√] displays the square root symbol and an open parenthesis.

- ⬚2nd⬚ [π] displays the special number π.

- ⬚2nd⬚ [ANS] recalls the answer from the previous calculation.

- ⬚2nd⬚ [e] displays the special number e.

- ⬚−⬚ denotes subtraction between two numbers while ⬚(−)⬚ denotes a negative sign.

Keystroke cross reference

0.1: 71 ⬚÷⬚ 7 ⬚+⬚ 3 ⬚∧⬚ 2 ⬚×⬚ 5

0.2: 4 ⬚(⬚ 2 ⬚+⬚ 1 ⬚)⬚

0.3: 17 ⬚÷⬚ ⬚(⬚ 5 ⬚+⬚ 3 ⬚)⬚

0.4: ⬚(⬚ 8 ⬚+⬚ 9 ⬚)⬚ ⬚÷⬚ ⬚(⬚ 7 ⬚+⬚ 2 ⬚)⬚

0.5: 3 ⬚∧⬚ ⬚(⬚ 2.7 ⬚×⬚ 1.8 ⬚)⬚

0.6: ⬚−⬚ is used for subtraction as in 9 ⬚−⬚ 6 while ⬚(−)⬚ is used to denote a negative number as in ⬚(−)⬚ 3 .

0.7: ⬚(−)⬚ 8 ⬚−⬚ 4

0.8: ⬚(⬚ 3 ⬚−⬚ 7 ⬚)⬚ ⬚÷⬚ ⬚(⬚ ⬚(−)⬚ 2 ⬚×⬚ 3 ⬚)⬚

0.9: 2 ⬚∧⬚ ⬚(−)⬚ 3

0.10: 2 ⬚∧⬚ ⬚−⬚ 3 gives a syntax error

0.11: | 2nd | [√] 11.4 | − | 3.5 |) | ÷ | 26.5

0.12: | (| 7 | × | 3 | ∧ | (−) | 2 | + | 1 |) | ÷ | (| 3 | − | 2 | ∧ | (−) | 3 |) |

0.13: | 2nd | [π]

0.14: | ENTER |

0.15: | 2nd | [e]

0.16: | 2nd | [ANS]

0.17: | (| 2nd | [√] 13 |) | − | 2nd | [√] 2 |) |) | ∧ | 3

0.18: | 2nd | [ANS] | + | 17 | ÷ | (| 2 | + | 2nd | [π] |) |

0.19: | (| 3 | ∧ | 2nd | [ANS] | + | 2 | ∧ | 2nd | [ANS] |) | ÷
| (| 5 | ∧ | 2nd | [ANS] | − | 4 | ∧ | 2nd | [ANS] |) |

0.20: 5000 | (| 1 | + | .07 | × | 10 |) |
or 5000 | × | (| 1 | + | .07 | × | 10 |) |

0.21: 5000 | × | 1.07 | ∧ | 10

0.22: 5000 | (| 1 | + | 2nd | [ANS] |) | ∧ | 120

TI-83 QUICK REFERENCE FOR CHAPTER 1

Keystroke cross reference

1.1: | (| 3 | ∧ | 2 | + | 1 |) | ÷ | 2nd | [√] 3 |) |

1.2: 1.0067 | ∧ | 48 | − | 1

1.3: 7800 | × | .0067 | × | 1.0067 | ∧ | 48 | ÷ | 2nd | [ANS]

1.4: 1.0058 | ∧ | 36 | − | 1

1.5: 5000 | × | .0058 | × | 1.0058 | ∧ | 36 | ÷ | 2nd | [ANS]

TI-83 QUICK REFERENCE FOR CHAPTER 2

TI-83 Instructions for Section 2.1
How to enter functions

Step 1: Press the $\boxed{Y=}$ key to get to the function screen.

Step 2: Use $\boxed{\text{CLEAR}}$ to delete any unwanted functions that appear.

Step 3: Enter your function using the $\boxed{X, T, \Theta, n}$ key for the variable.

TI-83 Instructions for Section 2.1
How to make a table of values

Step 1: Enter your function as described above.

Step 2: Press $\boxed{\text{2nd}}$ [TBLSET] to get to the TABLE SETUP menu.

Step 3: Set TblStart= to the starting place for the table.

Step 4: Set ΔTbl= to the increment value for the table.

Step 5: Press $\boxed{\text{2nd}}$ [TABLE] to view the table. The arrow keys $\boxed{\triangle}$ and $\boxed{\nabla}$ will let you see more of the table.

Keystroke cross reference

2.1: $\boxed{Y=}$ 6.21 $\boxed{\div}$ $\boxed{(}$ 0.035 $\boxed{+}$ 0.45 $\boxed{\wedge}$ $\boxed{X, T, \Theta, n}$ $\boxed{)}$

2.2: $\boxed{\text{2nd}}$ [TBLSET] TblStart=0 ΔTbl=5

2.3: $\boxed{Y=}$ 176 $\boxed{(}$ 1 $\boxed{-}$ .834 $\boxed{\wedge}$ $\boxed{X, T, \Theta, n}$ $\boxed{)}$

2.4: $\boxed{\text{2nd}}$ [TBLSET] TblStart=0 ΔTbl=5

2.5: $\boxed{\text{2nd}}$ [TABLE]

2.6: $\boxed{\nabla}$

2.7: $\boxed{Y=}$ $\boxed{X, T, \Theta, n}$ $\boxed{(}$ $\boxed{X, T, \Theta, n}$ $\boxed{-}$ 1 $\boxed{)}$ $\boxed{(}$ $\boxed{X, T, \Theta, n}$ $\boxed{-}$ 2 $\boxed{)}$ $\boxed{\div}$ 750 $\boxed{\times}$ $\boxed{(}$ 5 $\boxed{\div}$ 6 $\boxed{)}$ $\boxed{\wedge}$ $\boxed{X, T, \Theta, n}$

2.8: $\boxed{\text{2nd}}$ [TBLSET] TblStart=1 ΔTbl=1

2.9: $\boxed{\nabla}$

2.10: $\boxed{Y=}$ $\boxed{X,T,\Theta,n}$ $\boxed{(}$ 36 $\boxed{-}$ $\boxed{X,T,\Theta,n}$ $\boxed{)}$

2.11: $\boxed{\text{2nd}}$ [TBLSET] TblStart=1 ΔTbl=1

TI-83 Instructions for Section 2.2
How to make graphs

Step 1: Use the $\boxed{Y=}$ key to open the function input window.

Step 2: Enter the function using $\boxed{X,T,\Theta,n}$ for the variable.

Step 3: Determine an appropriate $\boxed{\text{WINDOW}}$ setup by using practical information you have about the function. A table of values can be helpful in choosing the vertical span.

Alternative Step 3: For some functions it is appropriate to bypass Step 3 and go directly to the ZStandard view using $\boxed{\text{ZOOM}}$ 6 .

TI-83 Instructions for Section 2.2
How to adjust graphs and get function values

1. For some graphs it is best to look first at the **ZStandard** viewing screen using $\boxed{\text{ZOOM}}$ 6 .

2. The $\boxed{\text{TRACE}}$ key will make the cursor follow the graph, and some function values can be read from the bottom of the screen.

3. To get more precise function values, first be sure $\boxed{\text{TRACE}}$ is on. Then type in the number you want and press $\boxed{\text{ENTER}}$. The cursor will move to the point you want and give the function value at the Y= prompt.

4. If a graph does not appear in the **ZStandard** screen, try $\boxed{\text{TRACE}}$ $\boxed{\text{ENTER}}$ to find and show the graph.

5. If you want to get a closer look near a point (zoom in), first move the cursor there, and then use $\boxed{\text{ZOOM}}$ 2 $\boxed{\text{ENTER}}$.

6. If you want to see a larger view (zoom out), use $\boxed{\text{ZOOM}}$ 3 $\boxed{\text{ENTER}}$.

7. Manual adjustment of the viewing screen can be made using $\boxed{\text{WINDOW}}$. The Xmin and Xmax values determine the horizontal span of the viewing screen. The Ymin and Ymax values determine the vertical span of the viewing screen. Proper values for Ymin and Ymax can often be found by looking at a table of values.

2.12: $\boxed{Y=}$ $\boxed{X,T,\Theta,n}$ $\boxed{\wedge}$ 2 $\boxed{-}$ 1

2.13: | GRAPH |

2.14: | ZOOM | and then select 6:ZStandard from the menu.

Note that the **ZStandard** view can be (and may have been) changed on your calculator.

If **ZStandard** does not show the picture we made, see p. 47 in Part II of this Guide.

2.15: | TRACE |

2.16: | TRACE | 3 | ENTER |

2.17: | $Y=$ | 22.75 | X,T,Θ,n | $-$ | 300

2.18: | ZOOM | 6

2.19: | WINDOW | Xmin=0 Xmax=25 Ymin= | (−) | 325 Ymax=300

2.20: | GRAPH |

2.21: | TRACE | 10 | ENTER |

2.22: | $Y=$ | 750 | $\div$ | (| 8 | X,T,Θ,n |) |

2.23: | 2nd | [TBLSET] TblStart=1 ΔTbl=2

2.24: | WINDOW | Xmin=1 Xmax=11 Ymin=0 Ymax=100

2.25: | GRAPH |

2.26: | TRACE | 7 | ENTER |

2.27: | $Y=$ | | X,T,Θ,n | $\div$ | 40

2.28: | WINDOW | Xmin=500 Xmax=1000 Ymin=0 Ymax=30

2.29: | $Y=$ | 13 | $\div$ | (| .93 | $\wedge$ | X,T,Θ,n | $+$ | .05 |) |

2.30: | $Y=$ | Type 260 on the Y$_2$= line. | GRAPH |

2.31: | $Y=$ | 235 | $-$ | 105 | 2nd | [e^x] | (−) | .3 | X,T,Θ,n |) |

2.32: | WINDOW | Xmin=0 Xmax=36 Ymin=100 Ymax=250

2.33: | $Y=$ | Y$_2$=200 | GRAPH |

2.34: | $Y=$ | Y$_3$=235 | GRAPH |

2.35: | $Y=$ | Y$_1$= 40 | $+$ | .29 | X,T,Θ,n | Y$_2$= 50 | $+$ | .14 | X,T,Θ,n |

2.36: | WINDOW | Xmin=0 Xmax=100 Ymin=20 Ymax=90

2.37: | $Y =$ | Move the cursor to the left of Y_2 and press | ENTER |

TI-83 Instructions for Section 2.4
How to solve an equation of the form *Left Side=Right Side*

Crossing Graphs Method

Step 1: Use | $Y =$ | to enter *Left Side* on the $Y_1 =$ line and *Right Side* on the $Y_2 =$ line.

Step 2: | GRAPH | and make necessary adjustments so that the crossing point shows on the graphing screen.

Step 3: Press | 2nd | [CALC] and select **5:intersect** from the menu.

Step 4: Press | ENTER | at each of the prompts **First curve?** and **Second curve?**.

Step 5: If there is only one crossing point on the screen, press | ENTER | at the **Guess?** prompt. If there is more than one crossing point on the screen, move the cursor near the one you want before pressing | ENTER | .

Step 6: At the **Intersection** prompt read the solution from the **X=** display.

Single Graph Method

Step 1: Write the equation as *Left Side−Right Side=* 0.

Step 2: Use | $Y =$ | to enter *Left Side−Right Side* as a single function.

Step 3: | GRAPH | and make necessary adjustments so that the zero is shown.

Step 4: Press | 2nd | [CALC] and select **2:zero** from the menu.

Step 5: At the **Left Bound?** prompt move the cursor to the left of the zero and press | ENTER | .

Step 6: At the **Right Bound?** prompt move the cursor to the right of the zero and press | ENTER | .

Step 7: At the **Guess?** prompt press | ENTER | .

Step 8: At the **Zero** prompt read the solution from the **X=** display.

2.38: | $Y =$ | $Y_1 =$ 800 | $-$ | 730 | 2nd | [e^x] | $(-)$ | .06 | X, T, Θ, n | $)$ |
  $Y_2 =$ 600

2.39: | WINDOW | Xmin=0 Xmax=30 Ymin=0 Ymax=700

2.40: | 2nd | [CALC] 5:intersect | ENTER | | ENTER | | ENTER |

2.41: | $Y =$ | 102 | $+$ | 12 | X, T, Θ, n | $-$ | 100 | 2nd | [e^x] .1 | X, T, Θ, n | $)$ |

2.42: | WINDOW | Xmin=0 Xmax=5 Ymin= | $(-)$ | 3 Ymax=5

2.43: 2nd [CALC] **2:zero** Move cursor left of zero ENTER .
Move cursor right of zero ENTER   ENTER

2.44: $Y =$ $Y_1 = 6.21$ ÷ (.035 + .45 ∧ X, T, Θ, n)

2.45: $Y =$ $Y_2 = 85$

2.46: 2nd [CALC] **5:intersect** ENTER   ENTER   ENTER

2.47: $Y =$ 62.4 2nd [π] X, T, Θ, n ∧ 2 (2 − X, T, Θ, n ÷ 3) − 436

2.48: 2nd [CALC] **2:zero** Move cursor left of zero ENTER
Move cursor right of zero ENTER   ENTER

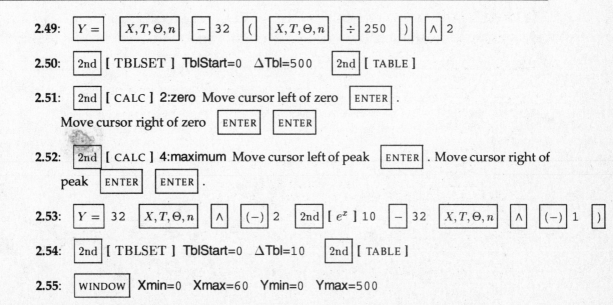

TI-83 Instructions for Section 2.5
How to locate maxima and minima on a graph

First graph the function and adjust the window as necessary so that the maxima and minima are clearly shown. Once this is done proceed as follows.

Step 1: Press 2nd [CALC] and select **3:minimum** or **4:maximum** from the menu.

Step 2: At the **Left Bound?** prompt move the cursor to the left of the maximum or minimum and then press ENTER .

Step 3: At the **Right Bound?** prompt move the cursor to the right of the maximum or minimum and then press ENTER .

Step 4: At the **Guess?** prompt press ENTER .

Step 5: At the **Minimum** or **Maximum** prompt read the location of the maximum or minimum from the bottom of the display.

2.49: $Y =$ X, T, Θ, n − 32 (X, T, Θ, n ÷ 250) ∧ 2

2.50: 2nd [TBLSET] TblStart=0 ΔTbl=500 2nd [TABLE]

2.51: 2nd [CALC] **2:zero** Move cursor left of zero ENTER .
Move cursor right of zero ENTER   ENTER

2.52: 2nd [CALC] **4:maximum** Move cursor left of peak ENTER . Move cursor right of peak ENTER   ENTER .

2.53: $Y =$ 32 X, T, Θ, n ∧ (−) 2 2nd [e^x] 10 − 32 X, T, Θ, n ∧ (−) 1)

2.54: 2nd [TBLSET] TblStart=0 ΔTbl=10 2nd [TABLE]

2.55: WINDOW Xmin=0 Xmax=60 Ymin=0 Ymax=500

2.55: [WINDOW] Xmin=0 Xmax=60 Ymin=0 Ymax=500

2.56: [2nd] [CALC] 4:maximum Move cursor left of maximum [ENTER] .
Move cursor right of maximum [ENTER] [ENTER] .

2.57: [Y =] Y_2= [2nd] [e^x] 10 [−] 32 [X, T, Θ, n] [∧] [(−)] 1 [ )]

2.58: [Y =] Put the cursor on the = sign on the Y_1 line and press [ENTER] .

2.59: [Y =] Highlight = on Y_1 line and press [ENTER] .
Highlight = on Y_2 line and press [ENTER] .

2.60: [WINDOW] Xmin= [(−)] 3750 Xmax=6250 Ymin= [(−)] 1150 Ymax=1650

2.61: [Y =] [( ] [X, T, Θ, n] [÷] 4 [ )] [∧] 2 [+] [( ] 100 [−] [X, T, Θ, n] [ )] [∧] 2
[÷] [( ] 4 [2nd] [π] [ )]

2.62: [2nd] [CALC] 3:minimum Move cursor left of minimum [ENTER] .
Move cursor right of minimum [ENTER] [ENTER] .

TI-83 QUICK REFERENCE FOR CHAPTER 3

Keystroke cross reference

3.1: $\boxed{Y =}$ 32 $\boxed{X, T, \Theta, n}$ $\boxed{-}$ 192

TI-83 Instructions for Section 3.3
How to set up statistical plots

Step 1: Press $\boxed{\text{2nd}}$ [STAT PLOT] .

Step 2: Select 1:Plot 1 from the menu.

Step 3: Use the arrow keys to highlight On and press $\boxed{\text{ENTER}}$.

Step 4: Check the other lines in this menu to see that they are correct. Usually you will want Xlist set to $\boxed{\text{2nd}}$ [L1] , indicating that the L1 column goes on the horizontal axis, and Ylist set to $\boxed{\text{2nd}}$ [L2] , indicating that the L2 list goes on the vertical axis.

<u>Note</u>: You do not have to turn on statistical plots each time you want to graph data. This setting remains in effect until you specifically turn it Off. To do so, proceed as above, but in Step 3, highlight Off. A plot can also be turned off from the function entry window: Press $\boxed{Y =}$ and then $\boxed{\triangle}$ to move to the top line. When a plot is on, its name is highlighted there. To change the status, place the cursor on the name and then press $\boxed{\text{ENTER}}$.

TI-83 Instructions for Section 3.3
How to enter data

Step 1: Press $\boxed{\text{STAT}}$.

Step 2: Select 1:Edit from the menu.

Step 3: If it is necessary to clear old data, highlight L1 and then press $\boxed{\text{CLEAR}}$ $\boxed{\text{ENTER}}$. Repeat this for each column as necessary.

Step 4: Locate the cursor in the column where you want to enter data and type each data entry followed by either $\boxed{\text{ENTER}}$ or $\boxed{\nabla}$.

TI-83 Instructions for Section 3.3
How to plot data points

Step 1: Be sure that statistical plotting is turned on and the Plot 1 screen properly configured as described above. Also you should use $\boxed{Y =}$ to check if old functions are stored and if necessary $\boxed{\text{CLEAR}}$ them.

Step 2: Enter your data points as described above. In the statistical plot setup outlined above, the L1 column corresponds to the horizontal axis, and the L2 column corresponds to the vertical axis.

Step 3: When data is properly entered use $\boxed{\text{ZOOM}}$ 9 to display automatically all data points on the screen.

3.2: $\boxed{\text{STAT}}$ 1:Edit Enter values for d in L1 column. Enter values for N in L2 column.

3.3: Turn statistical plots on using $\boxed{\text{2nd}}$ [STAT PLOT] 1:Plot1 Highlight On $\boxed{\text{ENTER}}$. In Xlist: type $\boxed{\text{2nd}}$ [L1] , and in Ylist: type $\boxed{\text{2nd}}$ [L2] . (You only need to do this the first time you plot. Statistical plotting will remain on until you turn it off.) $\boxed{\text{ZOOM}}$ 9 to make the graph.

3.4: $\boxed{Y =}$ 462 $\boxed{X, T, \Theta, n}$ $\boxed{+}$ 28321 $\boxed{\text{GRAPH}}$

3.5: $\boxed{\text{STAT}}$ 1:Edit Enter data for m in L1 column and data for F in L2 column.

3.6: Be sure statistical plotting is turned on and that the function list is clear. Now $\boxed{\text{ZOOM}}$ 9

3.7: $\boxed{Y =}$ 5 $\boxed{X, T, \Theta, n}$

3.8: $\boxed{\text{GRAPH}}$

TI-83 Instructions for Section 3.4
How to get a regression line

Step 1: Be sure your data points are properly entered in the L1 and L2 lists.

Step 2: Press $\boxed{\text{STAT}}$ and use $\boxed{\triangleright}$ to highlight CALC.

Step 3: Select 4:LinReg(ax+b) from the menu and press $\boxed{\text{ENTER}}$.

Step 4: You will see a screen that gives the equation of the regression line $y = ax + b$ and values for a and b. The given a value is the slope, and the given b value is the vertical intercept.

3.9: $\boxed{\text{STAT}}$ 1:Edit Enter t data in L1. Enter E data in L2.

(To make the graph, be sure $\boxed{\text{2nd}}$ [STAT PLOT] Plot1 is properly configured and $\boxed{\text{ZOOM}}$ 9 .)

3.10: With the data entered, press $\boxed{\text{STAT}}$. Move the highlight at the top of the screen to CALC. Select 4:LinReg(ax+b). Press $\boxed{\text{ENTER}}$ when returned to the calculation screen.

3.11: $\boxed{Y=}$ 1.21 $\boxed{X,T,\Theta,n}$ $\boxed{+}$ 27.46 $\boxed{\text{GRAPH}}$

3.12: $\boxed{\text{STAT}}$ 1:Edit Enter t values in L1 column and M values in the L2 column.

3.13: Use $\boxed{Y=}$ and be sure the function list is $\boxed{\text{CLEAR}}$. Use $\boxed{\text{2nd}}$ [STAT PLOT] and be sure Plot1 is On and that Xlist: is set to L1 and that Ylist: is set to L2. $\boxed{\text{ZOOM}}$ 9

3.14: $\boxed{\text{STAT}}$ CALC 4:LinReg(ax+b) $\boxed{\text{ENTER}}$

3.15: $\boxed{Y=}$ 12.89 $\boxed{X,T,\Theta,n}$ $\boxed{+}$ 252.62 $\boxed{\text{GRAPH}}$

3.16: $\boxed{Y=}$ $Y_1=$ $\boxed{(}$ 900 $\boxed{-}$ 28 $\boxed{X,T,\Theta,n}$ $\boxed{)}$ $\boxed{\div}$ 32
$Y_2=$ 3 $\boxed{X,T,\Theta,n}$

3.17: $\boxed{\text{WINDOW}}$ Xmin=0 Xmax=30 Ymin=0 Ymax=30

3.18: If you get extra dots on the screen, you may need to turn statistical plotting off using $\boxed{\text{2nd}}$ [STAT PLOT] 4:PlotsOff $\boxed{\text{ENTER}}$.

3.19: $\boxed{\text{2nd}}$ [CALC] 5:intersect $\boxed{\text{ENTER}}$ $\boxed{\text{ENTER}}$ $\boxed{\text{ENTER}}$

3.20: $\boxed{Y=}$ $Y_1=$ $\boxed{(}$ 56 $\boxed{-}$ 12 $\boxed{X,T,\Theta,n}$ $\boxed{)}$ $\boxed{\div}$ .5
$Y_2=$4 $\boxed{X,T,\Theta,n}$

3.21: $\boxed{\text{WINDOW}}$ Xmin=0 Xmax=5 Ymin=0 Ymax=20

3.22: $\boxed{\text{2nd}}$ [CALC] 5:intersect $\boxed{\text{ENTER}}$ $\boxed{\text{ENTER}}$ $\boxed{\text{ENTER}}$

TI-83 QUICK REFERENCE FOR CHAPTER 4

Keystroke cross reference

4.1: $\boxed{\text{WINDOW}}$ Xmin=0 Xmax=5 Ymin=0 Ymax=100000

4.2: $\boxed{\text{WINDOW}}$ Xmin=0 Xmax=5 Ymin=0 Ymax=3500

4.3: $\boxed{\text{2nd}}$ [CALC] 5:intersect $\boxed{\text{ENTER}}$ $\boxed{\text{ENTER}}$ $\boxed{\text{ENTER}}$

4.4: $\boxed{Y=}$ $Y_1=$ 64 $\boxed{-}$ 64 $\boxed{\times}$ .71 $\boxed{\wedge}$ $\boxed{X,T,\Theta,n}$ $Y_2=$ 57

4.5: $\boxed{\text{2nd}}$ [CALC] 5:intersect $\boxed{\text{ENTER}}$ $\boxed{\text{ENTER}}$ $\boxed{\text{ENTER}}$

4.6: $\boxed{Y=}$ Y$_1$= 6 $\boxed{+}$ 69 $\boxed{\times}$ .96 $\boxed{\wedge}$ $\boxed{X,T,\Theta,n}$ Y$_2$= 32

4.7: $\boxed{\text{2nd}}$ [CALC] 5:intersect $\boxed{\text{ENTER}}$ $\boxed{\text{ENTER}}$ $\boxed{\text{ENTER}}$

4.8: $\boxed{\text{STAT}}$ 1:Edit Enter x values in L1 column and y values in L2 column.

4.9: $\boxed{\text{2nd}}$ [STAT PLOT] and be sure Plot1 is On. Then $\boxed{\text{ZOOM}}$ 9 .

4.10: $\boxed{\text{STAT}}$ 1:Edit Highlight L3 $\boxed{\text{2nd}}$ [e^x] $\boxed{\text{2nd}}$ [L2] $\boxed{)}$ $\boxed{\text{ENTER}}$.

4.11: $\boxed{\text{2nd}}$ [STAT PLOT] 1:Plot1 Change Ylist to L3, then $\boxed{\text{ZOOM}}$ 9 .

4.12: $\boxed{\text{LN}}$ 7 $\boxed{)}$

4.13: $\boxed{\text{STAT}}$ 1:Edit Highlight L2 $\boxed{\text{LN}}$ $\boxed{\text{2nd}}$ [L3] $\boxed{)}$ $\boxed{\text{ENTER}}$.

4.14: $\boxed{\text{STAT}}$ 1:Edit Enter time in L1 column and population in L3 column.

4.15: $\boxed{\text{2nd}}$ [STAT PLOT] Set Plot1 to On. Set Xlist to L1 and Ylist to L3. $\boxed{\text{ZOOM}}$ 9 .

4.16: $\boxed{\text{STAT}}$ 1:Edit Highlight L2 and $\boxed{\text{LN}}$ $\boxed{\text{2nd}}$ [L3] $\boxed{)}$ $\boxed{\text{ENTER}}$.

4.17: $\boxed{\text{2nd}}$ [STAT PLOT] Plot1 change Ylist to L2. $\boxed{\text{ZOOM}}$ 9

4.18: $\boxed{\text{STAT}}$ CALC 4:LinReg(ax+b) $\boxed{\text{ENTER}}$

4.19: $\boxed{Y=}$ .0294 $\boxed{X,T,\Theta,n}$ $\boxed{+}$ 1.6747 $\boxed{\text{GRAPH}}$

4.20: $\boxed{\text{2nd}}$ [STAT PLOT] Plot1 Change Ylist to L3. $\boxed{Y=}$
5.3372 $\boxed{\times}$ 1.0298 $\boxed{\wedge}$ $\boxed{X,T,\Theta,n}$. Then $\boxed{\text{ZOOM}}$ 9 .

4.21: $\boxed{\text{STAT}}$ 1:Edit Enter t data in L1 column and C data in L3 column.

4.22: (You may need to use $\boxed{Y=}$ and $\boxed{\text{CLEAR}}$ out old functions.) $\boxed{\text{2nd}}$ [STAT PLOT]
Plot1 Set Ylist to L3. $\boxed{\text{ZOOM}}$ 9

4.23: $\boxed{\text{STAT}}$ 1:Edit Highlight L2. $\boxed{\text{LN}}$ $\boxed{\text{2nd}}$ [L3] $\boxed{)}$ $\boxed{\text{ENTER}}$

4.24: $\boxed{Y=}$ .095 $\boxed{X,T,\Theta,n}$ $\boxed{-}$ .351 $\boxed{\text{GRAPH}}$

4.25: $\boxed{\text{2nd}}$ [STAT PLOT] Plot1 Set Ylist to L3. $\boxed{Y=}$ .704 $\boxed{\times}$ 1.1 $\boxed{\wedge}$ $\boxed{X,T,\Theta,n}$
$\boxed{\text{ZOOM}}$ 9

4.26: $\boxed{\text{STAT}}$ 1:Edit Enter t data in L1 column and B data in L3 column.

4.27: $\boxed{\text{STAT}}$ 1:Edit Highlight L2. $\boxed{\text{LN}}$ $\boxed{\text{2nd}}$ [L3] $\boxed{)}$ $\boxed{\text{ENTER}}$

4.28: $\boxed{\text{2nd}}$ [TBLSET] TblStart=1 ΔTbl=1

4.29: $\boxed{\text{2nd}}$ [TBLSET] TblStart=215 ΔTbl=50

TI-83 QUICK REFERENCE FOR CHAPTER 5

Keystroke cross reference

5.1: $\boxed{Y =}$ 16 $\boxed{X,T,\Theta,n}$ $\boxed{\wedge}$ 2

5.2: $\boxed{\text{WINDOW}}$ Xmin=0 Xmax=5 Ymin=0 Ymax=100

5.3: $\boxed{\text{2nd}}$ [CALC] 5:intersect $\boxed{\text{ENTER}}$ $\boxed{\text{ENTER}}$ $\boxed{\text{ENTER}}$

5.4: $\boxed{Y =}$ 21.83 $\boxed{X,T,\Theta,n}$ $\boxed{\wedge}$ 0.18

5.5: $\boxed{Y =}$ (on Y_1 line) 5.34 $\boxed{\times}$ 1.03 $\boxed{\wedge}$ $\boxed{X,T,\Theta,n}$
         (on Y_2 line) 0.04 $\boxed{X,T,\Theta,n}$ $\boxed{\wedge}$ 1.5 $\boxed{+}$ 5.34

5.6: $\boxed{\text{2nd}}$ [TBLSET] TblStart=0 ΔTbl=5

5.7: $\boxed{\text{STAT}}$ 1:Edit Enter x data in L3 column. Highlight L4 and then 3 $\boxed{\text{2nd}}$ [L3] $\boxed{\wedge}$ 2

5.8: Highlight L1 $\boxed{\text{LN}}$ $\boxed{\text{2nd}}$ [L3] $\boxed{)}$

5.9: Highlight L2 $\boxed{\text{LN}}$ $\boxed{\text{2nd}}$ [L4] $\boxed{)}$

5.10: $\boxed{\text{2nd}}$ [STAT PLOT] 1:Plot1 On. Set Xlist: to L1 and Ylist: to L2. $\boxed{\text{ZOOM}}$ 9

5.11: $\boxed{\text{STAT}}$ CALC 4:LinReg(ax+b) $\boxed{\text{ENTER}}$

TI-83 Instructions for Section 5.2
How to fit power functions to data

The procedure is similar to the one used for exponential regression except we take the logarithm of the variable values in addition to the function values.

Step 1: Press ⬛STAT⬛ , select 1:Edit, and ⬛CLEAR⬛ out old lists as necessary. In the L3 column enter the values for the variable, and in the L4 column enter the corresponding values for the function. Now highlight L1 and type ⬛LN⬛ ⬛2nd⬛ [L3] ⬛)⬛ and then ⬛ENTER⬛ . Then highlight L2 and type ⬛LN⬛ ⬛2nd⬛ [L4] ⬛)⬛ and then ⬛ENTER⬛ .

Step 2: To plot the data on a logarithmic scale, press ⬛2nd⬛ [STAT PLOT] and select 1:Plot 1 from the menu. Highlight On and press ⬛ENTER⬛ . Make sure that Xlist is set to L1 and Ylist is set to L2. Use ⬛Y =⬛ and ⬛CLEAR⬛ old functions if necessary, then ⬛ZOOM⬛ 9 .

Step 3: Perform linear regression as usual: Press ⬛STAT⬛ and use ⬛▷⬛ to move the highlight at the top of the screen to CALC. Select 4:LinReg(ax+b), then press ⬛ENTER⬛ .

5.12: ⬛STAT⬛ 1:Edit and enter data

5.13: Highlight L1 and ⬛LN⬛ ⬛2nd⬛ [L3] ⬛)⬛ ⬛ENTER⬛ . Highlight L2 and ⬛LN⬛ ⬛2nd⬛ [L4] ⬛)⬛ ⬛ENTER⬛ .

5.14: ⬛2nd⬛ [STAT PLOT] 1:Plot 1 On. Set Xlist: to L1 and Ylist: to L2. ⬛ZOOM⬛ 9

5.15: ⬛STAT⬛ CALC 4:LinReg(ax+b) ⬛ENTER⬛ .

5.16: ⬛2nd⬛ [STAT PLOT] and set Xlist: to L3 and Ylist: to L4. ⬛Y =⬛ and enter 4.18 ⬛X, T, Θ, n⬛ ⬛∧⬛ 3 . Then ⬛ZOOM⬛ 9 .

5.17: ⬛STAT⬛ 1:Edit enter D values in L3 and P values in L4.

5.18: Highlight L1 ⬛LN⬛ ⬛2nd⬛ [L3] ⬛)⬛ . Highlight L2 ⬛LN⬛ ⬛2nd⬛ [L4] ⬛)⬛ .

5.19: ⬛STAT⬛ 1:Edit and enter data for L in L3 column

5.20: ⬛STAT⬛ 1:Edit and enter data for T in L4 column

5.21: Highlight L1. ⬛LN⬛ ⬛2nd⬛ [L3] ⬛)⬛

5.22: Highlight L2. ⬛LN⬛ ⬛2nd⬛ [L4] ⬛)⬛

5.23: ⬛2nd⬛ [STAT PLOT] Set Xlist: to L1 and Ylist: to L2 ⬛ZOOM⬛ 9

5.24: ⬛STAT⬛ CALC 4:LinReg(ax+b) ⬛ENTER⬛ .

5.25: Highlight L1   [LOG]   [2nd] [L3]   [ )] . Highlight L2   [LOG]   [2nd] [L4]   [ )] .

5.26: [Y =]   [SIN]   [X, T, Θ, n]   [ )]

5.27: [MODE] Degree [ENTER]

5.28: [Y =]   [COS]   [X, T, Θ, n]   [ )]

5.29: [Y =]   [TAN]   [X, T, Θ, n]   [ )]

TI-83 QUICK REFERENCE FOR CHAPTER 6

Keystroke cross reference

6.1: (Be sure [2nd] [STAT PLOT] Plot1 is set to Off.) [Y =] 30 [+] 18 [X, T, Θ, n] [−] 16 [X, T, Θ, n] [∧] 2 . [WINDOW] Xmin=0 Xmax=5 Ymin=0 Ymax=50 [GRAPH] .

6.2: [2nd] [CALC] 2:zero Move cursor left of zero [ENTER] . Move cursor right of zero [ENTER] [ENTER] .

6.3: [2nd] [CALC] 4:maximum Move cursor left of maximum [ENTER] . Move cursor right of maximum [ENTER] [ENTER] .

6.4: [Y =] Y_1= 72 [+] 118 [2nd] [e^x] [(−)] .06 [X, T, Θ, n] [ )]
Y_2= 130

6.5: [2nd] [CALC] 5:intersect [ENTER] [ENTER] [ENTER]

6.6: [Y =] .338 [X, T, Θ, n] [( ] 1 [−] [X, T, Θ, n] [÷] 2.4 [ )]

6.7: [2nd] [CALC] 2:zero
Move cursor left of zero [ENTER] . Move cursor right of zero [ENTER] [ENTER] .

6.8: [Y =] 32 [−] .1818 [X, T, Θ, n]

6.9: [WINDOW] Xmin=0 Xmax=250 Ymin= [(−)] 20 Ymax=35

TI-83 Instructions for Section 6.5
How to find rates of change for functions given by formulas

Step 1: Graph the function and make sure the desired point shows on the graphing screen.

Step 2: Use $\boxed{\text{2nd}}$ [CALC] and choose **6:dy/dx** . Type in the desired x value, then press $\boxed{\text{ENTER}}$.

6.10: $\boxed{Y=}$ 16 $\boxed{X,T,\Theta,n}$ $\boxed{\wedge}$ 2 $\boxed{\text{WINDOW}}$ Xmin=0 Xmax=5 Ymin=0 Ymax=300 $\boxed{\text{GRAPH}}$

6.11: $\boxed{\text{2nd}}$ [CALC] **6:dy/dx** Type 2.5 and $\boxed{\text{ENTER}}$

6.12: $\boxed{Y=}$ $\boxed{X,T,\Theta,n}$ $\boxed{-}$ 32 $\boxed{(}$ $\boxed{X,T,\Theta,n}$ $\boxed{\div}$ 300 $\boxed{)}$ $\boxed{\wedge}$ 2

6.13: $\boxed{\text{TRACE}}$ 734 $\boxed{\text{ENTER}}$

6.14: $\boxed{\text{2nd}}$ [CALC] **6:dy/dx** 734 $\boxed{\text{ENTER}}$

TI-83 QUICK REFERENCE FOR CHAPTER 7

Keystroke cross reference

7.1: $\boxed{\text{STAT}}$ **1:Edit** and $\boxed{\text{CLEAR}}$ out old lists as necessary. Enter t values in the L1 column and N values in the L3 column. Highlight L2 and type $\boxed{\text{LN}}$ $\boxed{\text{2nd}}$ [L3] $\boxed{)}$ $\boxed{\text{ENTER}}$.

7.2: Set Plot1 to On and $\boxed{\text{ZOOM}}$ 9 .

7.3: $\boxed{\text{STAT}}$ CALC **4:LinReg(ax+b)** $\boxed{\text{ENTER}}$

7.4: $\boxed{\text{STAT}}$ **1:Edit** and $\boxed{\text{CLEAR}}$ out old lists as necessary. Enter N values in the L1 column and values of $\frac{1}{N}\frac{dN}{dt}$ in the L2 column. Set Plot1 to On and $\boxed{\text{ZOOM}}$ 9 .

7.5: $\boxed{\text{STAT}}$ CALC **4:LinReg(ax+b)** $\boxed{\text{ENTER}}$

TI-83 Instructions for Section 7.3
How to generate survivorship curves

The procedure is similar to the one used for plotting with exponential regression. The two differences are the use of the common logarithm instead of the natural logarithm, and connecting the data points with line segments.

Step 1: Press STAT , select 1:Edit, and CLEAR out old lists as necessary. In the L1 column enter the x values from the life table, and in the L3 column enter the corresponding l_x values. Now highlight L2 and type LOG 2nd [L3]) and then ENTER .

Step 2: Press 2nd [STAT PLOT] and select 1:Plot 1 from the menu. Highlight On and press ENTER . To connect the data points on the graph, from the Type: list select the second type of plot (connected icon). Make sure that Xlist is set to L1 and Ylist is set to L2.

Step 3: Use Y = and CLEAR old functions if necessary, then ZOOM 9 .

Arithmetic Operations

The TI-83 and TI-83 are designed to make arithmetic calculations easy, and many will find that little if any instruction is really necessary. Often all that is needed is a bit of practice to gain familiarity with the operation of the keyboard, and when difficulties do occur, they may be traceable to problems with parentheses and grouping. These are at least partly mathematical in nature, and you are encouraged to read the Prologue of *Functions and Change*. The keystrokes for arithmetic operations on the TI-82 and TI-83 are virtually identical, but where they differ we will provide separate instructions. All but a few of the figures in this text were made using the TI-83, and the output from the TI-82 is sometimes slightly different. The first time this is encountered, special pictures are made from the TI-82 screen, but in general the output of the two calculators is very similar. Where the difference may cause confusion we have pointed out the differences that are to be expected.

PROLOGUE: BASIC CALCULATIONS

To perform a simple calculation such as $\frac{72}{9} + 3 \times 5$ on the TI-82/83, we type in the expression just as we might write it on paper: 72 $\boxed{\div}$ 9 $\boxed{+}$ 3 $\boxed{\times}$ 5 . This is displayed in Figure 2.1. To get the answer, we press $\boxed{\text{ENTER}}$, and we see 23 as expected in Figure 2.2. For some calculations you need to access special keys.

Figure 2.1: *Entering a simple calculation*

Figure 2.2: *Using* $\boxed{\text{ENTER}}$ *to complete the calculation*

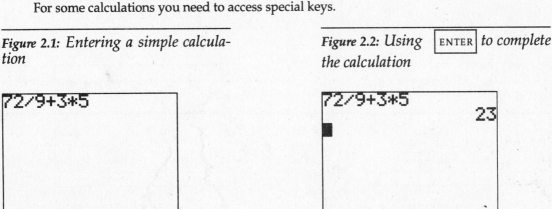

The exponent key: To enter an exponent like 2^3 you need to use the black $\boxed{\wedge}$ key located just below the $\boxed{\text{CLEAR}}$ key. Typing 2 $\boxed{\wedge}$ 3 $\boxed{\text{ENTER}}$ will produce the correct result, 8.

The square root key is at the top-left of the $\boxed{x^2}$ key.

TI-82

To access these *alternate keys*, you first press the blue $\boxed{\text{2nd}}$ key and the cursor will be replaced by a flashing, upward-pointing, arrow. Now press the $\boxed{x^2}$ key, and the square root symbol will appear on the display. In what follows we will use $\boxed{\text{2nd}}$ [$\sqrt{}$] to indicate this sequence of keystrokes. So for example, if you want to get $\sqrt{7}$, you type $\boxed{\text{2nd}}$ [$\sqrt{}$] 7 $\boxed{\text{ENTER}}$. The answer, 2.645751311, is shown in the figure below.

$$\sqrt{7} \qquad 2.645751311$$

TI-83

To access these *alternate keys*, you first press the gold $\boxed{\text{2nd}}$ key and the cursor will be replaced by a flashing, upward pointing arrow. Now press the $\boxed{x^2}$ key, and the square root symbol will appear on the display. The TI-83 automatically adds a left parenthesis following the square root symbol in anticipation of a longer expression. To complete your entry, you should remember to finish with $\boxed{)}$. In what follows we will use $\boxed{\text{2nd}}$ [$\sqrt{}$] to indicate this sequence of keystrokes. So for example, if you want to get $\sqrt{7}$, you type $\boxed{\text{2nd}}$ [$\sqrt{}$] 7 $\boxed{)}$ $\boxed{\text{ENTER}}$. The answer is shown in Figure 2.3.

The number π: The special number π is printed above the $\boxed{\wedge}$ key. To access it you use $\boxed{\text{2nd}}$ [π] . When you do this, the calculator will display the symbol for π as shown in the first line of Figure 2.4. When you press $\boxed{\text{ENTER}}$, the calculator will display the numerical approximation shown in the second line of Figure 2.4.

Figure 2.3: Using the square root key

Figure 2.4: Accessing π

$$\sqrt{(7)} \qquad 2.645751311$$

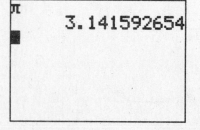

$$\pi \qquad 3.141592654$$

The number *e***:**

TI-82

The special number *e* is most often used in the context of an *exponential function*. For this reason, when you press 2nd [e^x] (above the black LN key) the calculator automatically adds the ∧ in anticipation of an exponent. To get the number $e = e^1$ we provide an exponent of 1. That is, we type 2nd [e^x] 1 and ENTER . The result, 2.718281828, is the numerical approximation of *e* shown below.

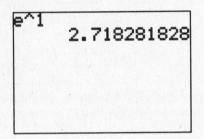

TI-83

The special number *e* appears in gold above the division key ÷ . You access it using 2nd [*e*] and ENTER . The result, 2.718281828, is a numerical approximation of *e* which is shown in Figure 2.6.

We should note however that this number is most often used in the context of an *exponential function*, and this provides an alternative way of getting the number *e*. While this method takes more keystrokes, it is the way *e* will be most commonly accessed in what follows. There is a second key 2nd [e^x] (above the black LN key) which automatically adds the ∧ and a left parenthesis in anticipation of an exponent. To get the number $e = e^1$ using this key we use 2nd [e^x] 1) and ENTER . The result, which matches our first approximation of *e* in Figure 2.6, is in Figure 2.5.

Figure 2.5: ∧ *(and (on the TI-83) automatically displayed when you use* 2nd [e^x]

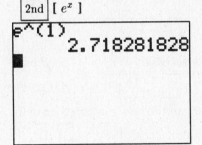

Figure 2.6: *Using* 2nd [*e*] *to access* e *directly (not available on the TI-82)*

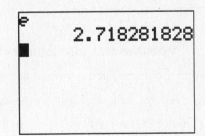

PROLOGUE: PARENTHESES

Two of the most important keys on your calculator are the black parentheses keys $($
and $)$. When parentheses are indicated in a calculation, you should use them, and sometimes it is necessary to add additional parentheses. To make a calculation such as $2.7(3.6+1.8)$
you type 2.7 $($ 3.6 $+$ 1.8 $)$ and then ENTER . The result is shown in Figure 2.7.
To calculate $\dfrac{2.7 - 3.3}{6.1 + 4.7}$, we must use parentheses around $2.7 - 3.3$ to indicate that the whole
expression goes in the numerator, and we must use parentheses around $6.1 + 4.7$ to indicate
that the whole expression goes in the denominator. Thus we type

$($ 2.7 $-$ 3.3 $)$ $\div$ $($ 6.1 $+$ 4.7 $)$ and ENTER .

The result is in Figure 2.8.

Figure 2.7: A calculation using paren-
theses

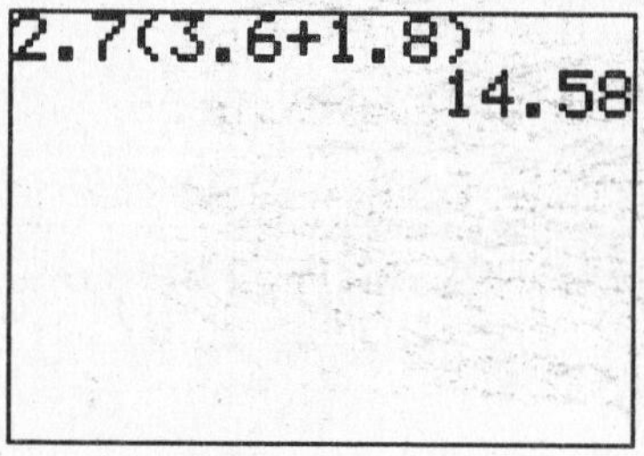

```
2.7(3.6+1.8)
           14.58
```

Figure 2.8: A calculation where addi-
tional parentheses must be supplied

```
(2.7-3.3)/(6.1+4
.7)
        -.0555555556
```

When you are in doubt about whether parentheses are necessary or not, it is good prac-
tice to use them. For example, if you calculate $\dfrac{3 \times 4}{7}$ using 3 $\times$ 4 $\div$ 7 , you will get the
right answer, 1.71. You will get the same answer if you use parentheses to emphasize to the
calculator that the entire expression 3×4 goes in the numerator: $($ 3 $\times$ 4 $)$ $\div$ 7 .
If on the other hand you calculate $\dfrac{7}{3 \times 4}$, you must use parentheses to get the correct answer,
0.58. The correct entry is 7 $\div$ $($ 3 $\times$ 4 $)$. If you leave out the parentheses, using
7 $\div$ 3 $\times$ 4 , your calculator will think that only the 3 goes in the denominator, and you
will get the wrong answer.

The use of parentheses leaves no room for doubt about what goes where, and their correct use is essential to the operation of the calculator.

PROLOGUE: MINUS SIGNS

If you look on your TI-82/83 keyboard, you will find two minus signs. One is the blue key $\boxed{-}$ located just above the $\boxed{+}$ key. The other is the $\boxed{(-)}$ key that is just to the left of the $\boxed{\text{ENTER}}$ key. The $\boxed{-}$ key is used for subtraction as in 9 $\boxed{-}$ 4 while the $\boxed{(-)}$ key is used to denote a negative number. For example if you want to get 2^{-3} you must use 2 $\boxed{\wedge}$ $\boxed{(-)}$ 3 as shown in Figure 2.9. If you try to use 2 $\boxed{\wedge}$ $\boxed{-}$ 3 you will get a *syntax error* as seen in Figure 2.10.

Figure 2.9: *Using* $\boxed{(-)}$ *to calculate* 2^{-3}

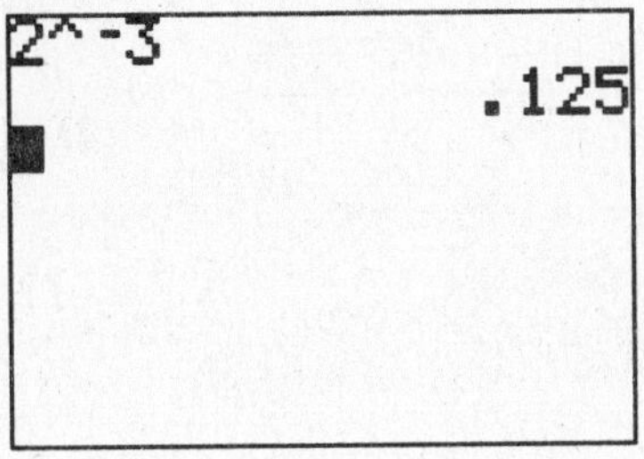

```
2^-3
            .125
■
```

Figure 2.10: *Syntax error displayed when* $\boxed{-}$ *is used in* 2^{-3}

```
ERR:SYNTAX
1■Quit
2:Goto
```

The mathematical distinction between the subtraction operation and the sign of a number is discussed more fully in the Prologue of *Functions and Change*. Briefly, you use the subtraction key $\boxed{-}$ when two numbers are involved, and you use the minus key $\boxed{(-)}$ when only one number is involved. With a little practice, the distinction is easy.

PROLOGUE: CHAIN CALCULATIONS

Some calculations are most naturally done in stages. The TI-82/83 $\boxed{\text{2nd}}$ [ANS] key is helpful here. This key refers to the results of the last calculation. To show its use, let's look at

$$\left(\frac{2+\pi}{7}\right)^{\left(3+\frac{7}{9}\right)}$$

This can be done in a single calculation, but we will show how to do it in two steps. First we calculate the exponent $3 + \frac{7}{9}$ as shown in Figure 2.11. To finish, we need

$$\left(\frac{2+\pi}{7}\right)^{\text{Answer from the last calculation}}$$

The answer from the last calculation is obtained using [2nd] [ANS] . Thus to complete the calculation, we use [( ] [( ] 2 + [2nd] [π] [ )] [÷] 7 [ )] [∧] [2nd] [ANS] .
The completed calculation is in Figure 2.12.

Figure 2.11: *The first step in a chain calculation*

```
3+7/9
        3.777777778
```

Figure 2.12: *Completing a chain calculation using* [2nd] [ANS]

```
3+7/9
        3.777777778
((2+π)/7)^Ans
        .311728397
```

Making Tables and Graphs

The feature of modern calculators which makes them different from their forerunners is their ability to make tables and produce graphs. This is a significant technological step, but more importantly it enhances the calculator's utility as a mathematical and scientific problem-solving tool.

CHAPTER 2: MAKING TABLES OF VALUES

For a function given by a formula, we can always produce a hand-generated table of values by calculating many individual function values, but the TI-82/83 acts as a significant time saver by making such tables automatically.

Three steps are required to make tables of values on a calculator. We will show them in an example. Let's make a table of values for $f = 3x + 1$.

Step 1, Entering the function: The first step is to tell the calculator which function we are using. To do this we use $\boxed{Y =}$ to show the *function entry* window. The TI-82/83 remembers functions that have been entered before, and so when you do this, you may find leftover formulas already on the screen as shown in Figure 2.13. If so, move the cursor to each formula that appears and press $\boxed{\text{CLEAR}}$. After the clean-up, you should have a clear function entry window like the one in Figure 2.14. (The TI-82 will not show Plot1 Plot2 Plot3 at the top of the screen, nor will it show the marks to the left of the Y's.) The presence of the lines $Y_1 =$ through $Y_7 =$ in Figure 2.14 indicates that many functions

Figure 2.13: *Clutter from previous work left on the function entry screen*	**Figure 2.14**: *Using* $\boxed{\text{CLEAR}}$ *to clean up the function entry window*

can be entered. For the moment, we will only use $Y_1 =$. Now we enter the function.[1]

---

[1] The TI-82 uses $\boxed{X, T, \Theta}$ to enter variables, while the TI-83 uses $\boxed{X, T, \Theta, n}$. On this first occurrence, we

TI-82

To enter the function, we use $\boxed{X,T,\Theta}$ for the variable x. (We would use the $\boxed{X,T,\Theta}$ key no matter what the name of the variable in our function.) Thus on the $Y_1=$ line we type 3 $\boxed{X,T,\Theta}$ $\boxed{+}$ 1 . The properly entered function is in Figure 2.15. Notice that the calculator writes the variable x as X. Once again, this is the symbol that the calculator will display no matter what the name of our variable.

TI-83

To enter the function, we use $\boxed{X,T,\Theta,n}$ for the variable x. (We would use the $\boxed{X,T,\Theta,n}$ key no matter what the name of the variable in our function.) Thus on the $Y_1=$ line we type 3 $\boxed{X,T,\Theta,n}$ $\boxed{+}$ 1 . The properly entered function is in Figure 2.15. Notice that the calculator writes the variable x as X. Once again, this is the symbol that the calculator will display no matter what the name of our variable.

Step 2, Setting up the table: The next step is to tell the calculator how we want the table to look. We do this using $\boxed{2nd}$ [TBLSET] . When you press $\boxed{2nd}$ [TBLSET] you should see the TABLE SETUP menu shown in Figure 2.16. The first option on the screen.[2]

Figure **2.15**: *The completed entry of* $3x + 1$

```
Plot1 Plot2 Plot3
\Y1■3X+1
\Y2=
\Y3=
\Y4=
\Y5=
\Y6=
\Y7=
```

Figure **2.16**: *The completed* TABLE SETUP *menu*

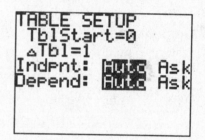

is TblStart=. This is where the table is to start. We want this table to start at $x = 0$, and so we enter 0 there. The next option is ΔTbl=. This gives the increment for the table. For the first view, we will look at the table for $x = 1, 2, 3, \ldots$. That is, we want to increment x by 1 at each step. (We will see later what happens if a different value for ΔTbl= is used.) Thus we type 1 here. The properly completed TABLE SETUP menu is in Figure 2.16.

Step 3, Viewing the table: To view the table we press $\boxed{2nd}$ [TABLE] , and the calculator will present the display shown in Figure 2.17. To get information from the table, it is important to remember that the X column corresponds to the variable x, and the Y_1 column gives the corresponding function value $f(x)$. Thus the first line in Figure 2.17 tells us that $f(0) = 1$, the second that $f(1) = 4$, and so on. There is more to the table than is

---

will separate our instructions to accommodate this, but since these keys are so similar, in what follows we will use $\boxed{X,T,\Theta,n}$ exclusively without direct reference to the TI-82 $\boxed{X,T,\Theta}$ key.

[2]On the TI-82 this appears as TblMin= As with $\boxed{X,T,\Theta}$ and $\boxed{X,T,\Theta,n}$, we will not distinguish between them in what follows.

shown on the screen. If you use $\boxed{\nabla}$ or $\boxed{\triangle}$, you will see additional entries. In Figure 2.18 we have used $\boxed{\nabla}$ to view further function values.

Figure 2.17: *A table of values for* $3x + 1$

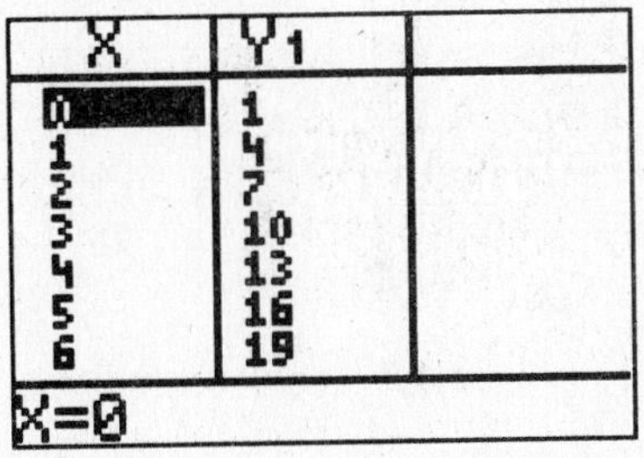

Figure 2.18: *Extending the table using* $\boxed{\nabla}$

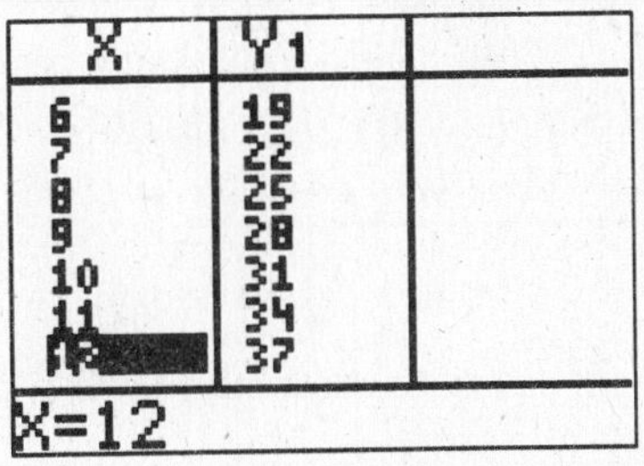

X	Y₁	

X	Y1	
0	1	
1	4	
2	7	
3	10	
4	13	
5	16	
6	19	

X=0

X	Y1	
6	19	
7	22	
8	25	
9	28	
10	31	
11	34	
12	37	

X=12

Adjusting the table: Many times we can see what we want from a table by making adjustments with $\boxed{\triangle}$ or $\boxed{\nabla}$, but for some alterations, this is impractical or impossible. Suppose for example that we wanted to see what happens for $x = 300, 301, 302, \ldots$ It not very efficient to do this using the $\boxed{\nabla}$ key. A better strategy is to use $\boxed{\text{2nd}}$ [TBLSET] to return to the TABLE SETUP menu and set TblStart= 300 . This is shown in Figure 2.19. Now when we use $\boxed{\text{2nd}}$ [TABLE] to go back to the table, the new TblStart= value causes the entries to start at $x = 300$ as shown in Figure 2.20.

Figure 2.19: *Changing* TblStart= *to* 300

Figure 2.20: *The table with a new starting value*

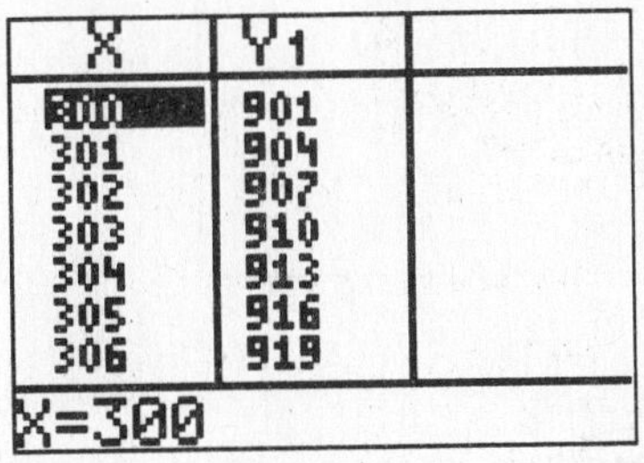

```
TABLE SETUP
 TblStart=300
 △Tbl=1
Indpnt: Auto Ask
Depend: Auto Ask
```

X	Y1	
300	901	
301	904	
302	907	
303	910	
304	913	
305	916	
306	919	

X=300

Let's make another adjustment which will allow us to view the table for $x = 0, 5, 10, 15, \ldots$. That is, we want to view a table for f which starts at $x = 0$ and has an increment of 5. To do this, we use $\boxed{\text{2nd}}$ [TBLSET] to return to the TABLE SETUP menu and then use TblStart=0 and ΔTbl=5 . The correctly configured TABLE SETUP menu is in Figure 2.21, and when we press $\boxed{\text{2nd}}$ [TABLE] , we see the new table in Figure 2.22.

Comparing functions: The calculator's ability to deal with more than one function allows us to use tables to make comparisons. For example, let's show how to compare the values of

Figure 2.21: *Changing the value of* $\triangle Tbl=$

```
TABLE SETUP
 TblStart=0
 ▵Tbl=5▪
Indpnt: Auto Ask
Depend: Auto Ask
```

Figure 2.22: *The table with an increment of 5*

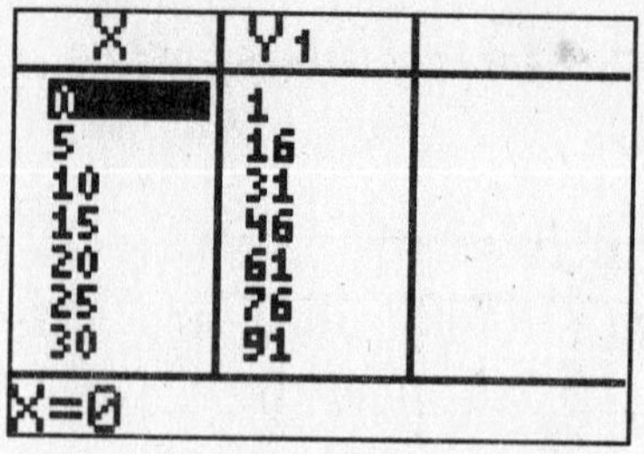

X	Y₁	
0	1	
5	16	
10	31	
15	46	
20	61	
25	76	
30	91	
X=0		

$f = 3x + 1$ with those of $g = 4x - 2$. First we need to use $\boxed{Y =}$ to enter the formula for g. We want to keep f as entered on the $Y_1 =$ line, so we don't clear it but move the cursor directly to the $Y_2 =$ line. There we enter 4 $\boxed{X, T, \Theta, n}$ $\boxed{-}$ 2 as shown in Figure 2.23. Use **TABLE SETUP** values of TblStart=0 and $\triangle$Tbl=1 . When we press $\boxed{2nd}$ [TABLE] , we see the table in Figure 2.24, which shows function values for f in the Y_1 column and values for g in the Y_2 column. Note that f starts out larger than g. They have the same value when $x = 3$, and after that g has the larger values.

Figure 2.23: *Entering a second function*

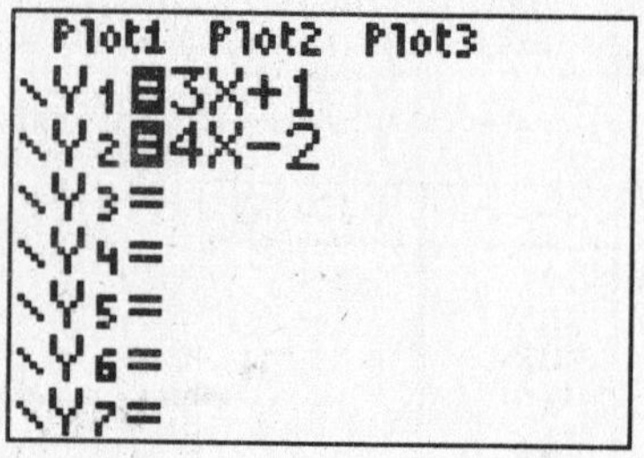

```
Plot1 Plot2 Plot3
\Y1☐3X+1
\Y2☐4X-2
\Y3=
\Y4=
\Y5=
\Y6=
\Y7=
```

Figure 2.24: *Comparing function values*

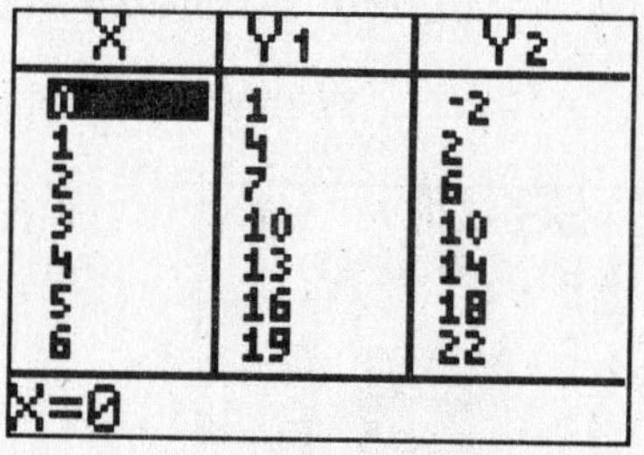

X	Y₁	Y₂
0	1	-2
1	4	2
2	7	6
3	10	10
4	13	14
5	16	18
6	19	22
X=0		

CHAPTER 2: GRAPHS

The TI-82/83 can generate the graph of a function as easily as it makes tables. We will illustrate using $f = \dfrac{x^4}{50} - x$. The first step is to tell the calculator which function we want to graph. We do this using the $\boxed{Y =}$ key exactly as we did in the previous section. Use $\boxed{\text{CLEAR}}$ to delete old functions and enter the new one on the Y_1 line using $\boxed{X, T, \Theta, n}$ $\boxed{\wedge}$ 4 $\boxed{\div}$ 50 $\boxed{-}$ $\boxed{X, T, \Theta, n}$. As with tables, the TI-82 chooses its own names for functions and variables; in this case Y_1 , which will appear on the vertical axis for f, and X, which will appear on the horizontal axis for x.

Once the function is properly entered as in Figure 2.25, we press $\boxed{\text{ZOOM}}$ and the menu shown in Figure 2.26 is shown. From this menu, select 6:ZStandard and the graph in Figure 2.27 will be shown.[3]

Figure 2.25: Using $\boxed{Y=}$ *to enter* $\dfrac{x^4}{50} -$ x

```
Plot1  Plot2  Plot3
\Y1 BX^4/50-X
\Y2=
\Y3=
\Y4=
\Y5=
\Y6=
\Y7=
```

Figure 2.26: Using $\boxed{\text{ZOOM}}$ *to get to the* ZOOM *menu*

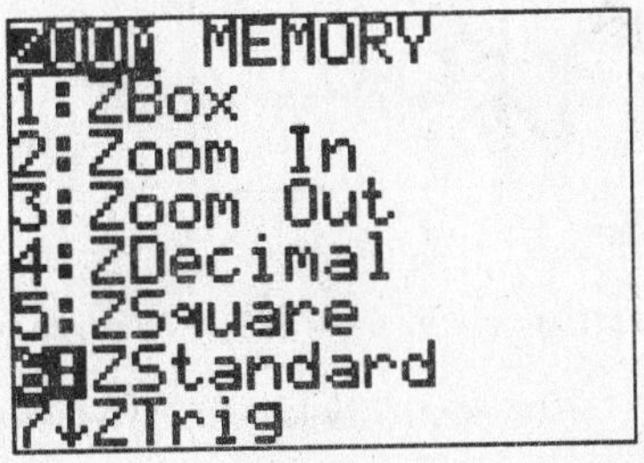

```
ZOOM  MEMORY
1:ZBox
2:Zoom In
3:Zoom Out
4:ZDecimal
5:ZSquare
6 ZStandard
7↓ZTrig
```

There are various ways of adjusting the picture shown by the calculator, and the TI-82/83 remembers the settings it used the last time it made a graph. The instructions we gave made what is called the ZStandard view. In this view, the horizontal span is from -10 to 10, and so is the vertical span. If your picture does not match the one in Figure 2.27, use $\boxed{Y=}$ to check that your function is properly entered. If this fails, refer to the *Graphics configuration notes* in the section entitled Chapter 2: Graphics configuration notes below. *It is important that you make your picture match the one in Figure 2.27; otherwise, you will have difficulty following the examples and explanations in what follows.*

Once we have a graph on the screen there are several ways to adjust the view or to get information from it.

Tracing the graph: The $\boxed{\text{TRACE}}$ key places a cursor on the graph and enables the left and right arrow keys, $\boxed{\triangleleft}$ and $\boxed{\triangleright}$, to move the cursor along the graph. (If there is more than one graph on the screen then $\boxed{\triangle}$ or $\boxed{\triangledown}$ moves the cursor to other graphs.) As the cursor moves, its location is recorded at the bottom of the screen. The X= prompt shows where we are on the horizontal axis, and the Y= prompt shows where we are on the vertical axis. In Figure 2.28 we have used $\boxed{\text{TRACE}}$ and moved the cursor to the lowest point of the graph, and we see X=2.3404255 and Y=-1.740345 at the bottom of

---

[3]This assumes the calculator is in its default graphics display mode. As is explained in what follows, this mode may have been altered by any number of calculator operations. Instructions for returning the calculator to its default display mode are given in the section entitled Chapter 2: Graphics configuration notes below.

the screen. This tells us that the cursor is located at the point $(2.3404255, -1.740345)$. Since this point lies on the graph it also tells us that, rounded to two decimal places, $f(2.34) = -1.74$.

Figure 2.27: *The graph of $\dfrac{x^4}{50} - x$*

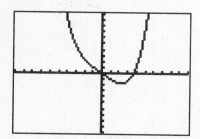

Figure 2.28: *Using* TRACE *to locate the cursor at the bottom of the graph*

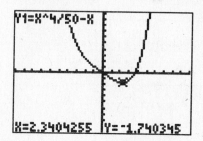

Getting function values: If we want to use TRACE to get the value of say $f(3)$, we might use the arrow keys to try to make the cursor land exactly on X=3. But if we do this, we find that the arrow keys make the X= prompt skip 3, going from 2.9787234 to 3.1914894. Both the TI-82 and the TI-83 offer us a way to correct this and make the cursor go exactly to X=3, but the keystrokes to accomplish this are different for the two calculators.

TI-82

We first press 2nd [CALC]. You will see the CALCULATE menu shown in Figure 2.29. We want a function value, so we choose 1:value from the menu. We will be returned to the graph with the prompt Eval X= at the bottom of the screen as shown in Figure 2.30. We are interested in $x = 3$, so we type in 3 as seen in Figure 2.31. Now when we press ENTER we see that the cursor has indeed moved to X=3, and read from Figure 2.32 that $f(3) = -1.38$.

TI-83

Be sure the TRACE option is on. Now type 3, and X=3 will appear at the bottom of the screen as shown in Figure 2.33. When we press enter, the cursor will move to X=3 as shown in Figure 2.34, and we read from the bottom of the screen that $f(3) = -1.38$.

Figure 2.29: *The TI-82* CALCULATE *menu*

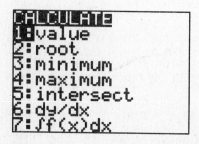

Figure 2.30: *The TI-82* Eval X= *prompt*

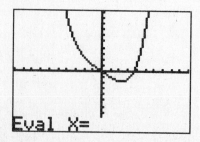

Figure 2.31: *Entering* X=3 *on the TI-82*

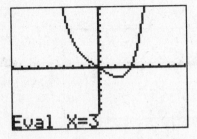

Figure 2.32: *Evaluating f at x = 3 on the TI-82*

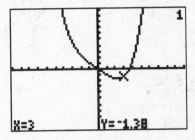

Figure 2.33: *Entering* X=3 *on the TI-83*

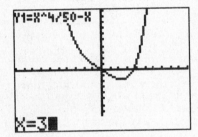

Figure 2.34: *Evaluating f at x = 3 on the TI-83*

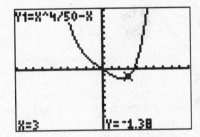

We should note that this only works if the X value you are looking for is actually on the viewing screen. If the X value you want is not far to the right or left of the viewing screen, you can use TRACE and move toward it. When the tracing cursor gets to the edge of the viewing area, the screen will change to follow it. If the X value is far to the right or left of the viewing area, you will need first to adjust the screen manually as described in **Manual window adjustments** below.

Zooming in and out: Figure 2.27 doesn't show much detail near the bottom of the graph, but the TI-82/83 can provide you with a closer look. Be sure you are using TRACE and put the cursor as near as you can to X=2.34. Now press ZOOM , and you will see the ZOOM menu shown in Figure 2.35. Select **2:Zoom In** from the menu. You will be put back in the graphing screen with nothing changed. To complete the zoom process, press ENTER , and the graph will be redrawn with a closer view as seen in Figure 2.36. Zooming turns off the trace, and so you will need to TRACE again to put the cursor back on the graph. If you ZOOM 2 ENTER again you will see a still closer view of the graph. To back away from the graph, press ZOOM and select **3:Zoom Out** from the menu. As before, we press ENTER to complete the zoom process, and then TRACE to put the cursor back on the graph.

Using TRACE ENTER **to find lost graphs**: There are some graphs which will not be shown

Figure 2.35: The ZOOM *menu*

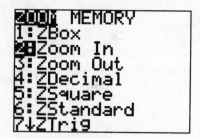

Figure 2.36: Zooming in near X=2.34

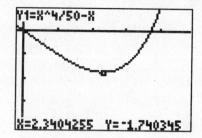

in the ZStandard view, and adjustments are required to show them. To illustrate this, let's make the graph of $f(x) = x^2 + 1000$. Use $\boxed{Y=}$ and $\boxed{\text{CLEAR}}$ out the old functions. On the $Y_1=$ line type $\boxed{X,T,\Theta,n}$ $\boxed{\wedge}$ 2 $\boxed{+}$ 1000 . Now if we $\boxed{\text{ZOOM}}$ 6 , we will see the axes but no graph at all as shown in Figure 2.37. The difficulty is that this graph sits high above the horizontal axis and is out of the viewing area. Press $\boxed{\text{TRACE}}$ to put the cursor onto the graph. Now if you press $\boxed{\text{ENTER}}$, the viewing area will move to find the cursor and hence the graph. The resulting graph is shown in Figure 2.38.

Figure 2.37: A lost graph

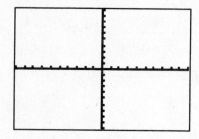

Figure 2.38: Finding a lost graph with $\boxed{\text{TRACE}}$ $\boxed{\text{ENTER}}$

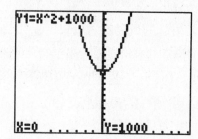

Manual window adjustments: You can get satisfactory views of many graphs by tracing and zooming, but some need manual adjustments. To illustrate this, let's look at the graph of $f(x) = \dfrac{x}{50}$. Use $\boxed{Y=}$ and $\boxed{\text{CLEAR}}$ out the old functions. Now type $\boxed{X,T,\Theta,n}$ $\boxed{\div}$ 50 and $\boxed{\text{ZOOM}}$ 6 to get the ZStandard view shown in Figure 2.39. (We have also pressed $\boxed{\text{TRACE}}$ so that the TI-83 will identify the graph in the upper-left corner of the screen. The TI-82 identifies graphs by placing a single number n corresponding to Y_n in the upper-right corner.) This is not a very good picture of the graph. The difficulty is that the graph is a straight line that in the ZStandard view lies so close to the horizontal axis that the calculator has difficulty distinguishing them.

This is a problem that is not easily fixed by zooming. We want to adjust the vertical span of the window to get a better view. We will make a table of values to help us choose an appropriate window size. Since the ZStandard window has a horizontal span of -10 to 10, we make the table start at -10 with an increment of 4. The result is shown in Figure 2.40, and it shows that as x ranges from -10 to 10, $f(x)$ ranges from -0.2 to 0.2.

Figure 2.39: *An unsatisfactory view of a line*

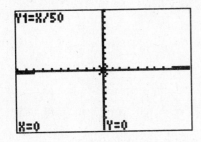

Figure 2.40: *A table of values for* $\dfrac{x}{50}$

X	Y1	
-10	-.2	
-6	-.12	
-2	-.04	
2	.04	
6	.12	
10	.2	
14	.28	
X=-10		

Allowing a little extra room, we want to change the vertical span so that it goes from -1 to 1. To accomplish this, we first press the $\boxed{\text{WINDOW}}$ key to get the WINDOW menu shown in Figure 2.41. The first two lines of this screen, Xmin=-10 and Xmax=10, make the graphing screen span from -10 to 10 in the horizontal direction. We will leave these settings as they are. The fourth and fifth lines, Ymin=-10 and Ymax=10, make the graphing screen span from -10 to 10 in the vertical direction. The arrow keys, $\boxed{\triangle}$ and $\boxed{\triangledown}$, will allow us to position the cursor so that we can change these to Ymin= $\boxed{(-)}$ 1 , and Ymax=1 . (Be sure to use $\boxed{(-)}$ rather than $\boxed{-}$ for these entries.) These new settings, which are shown in Figure 2.42, will make the viewing screen span from -10 to 10 in the horizontal direction and from -1 to 1 in the vertical direction. Now $\boxed{\text{GRAPH}}$ to get the

Figure 2.41: *The WINDOW menu*

```
WINDOW
 Xmin=-10
 Xmax=10
 Xscl=1
 Ymin=-10
 Ymax=10
 Yscl=1
 Xres=1
```

Figure 2.42: *Changing the vertical span*

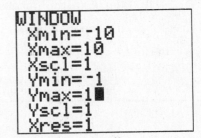

better view of the line shown in Figure 2.43.

The text gives instructions on how to use a table of values to choose the graphing window in practical settings. See Section 2 in Chapter 2 of *Functions and Change*.

Figure 2.43: *A better view of the line*

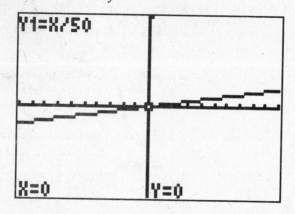

Showing more than one graph: To show multiple graphs, all you need to do is to enter each function you want to show on the function entry screen. For example, if we want to see the graphs of $f = x^2$ and $g = 5 - x^2$ at the same time, we first use $\boxed{Y =}$ and type $\boxed{X, T, \Theta, n}$ $\boxed{\wedge}$ 2 on the $Y_1 =$ line and 5 $\boxed{-}$ $\boxed{X, T, \Theta, n}$ $\boxed{\wedge}$ 2 on the $Y_2 =$ line as shown in Figure 2.44. Now if we use $\boxed{\text{ZOOM}}$ 6 we get the **ZStandard** view of both graphs shown in Figure 2.45.

Figure 2.44: *Entering two functions*

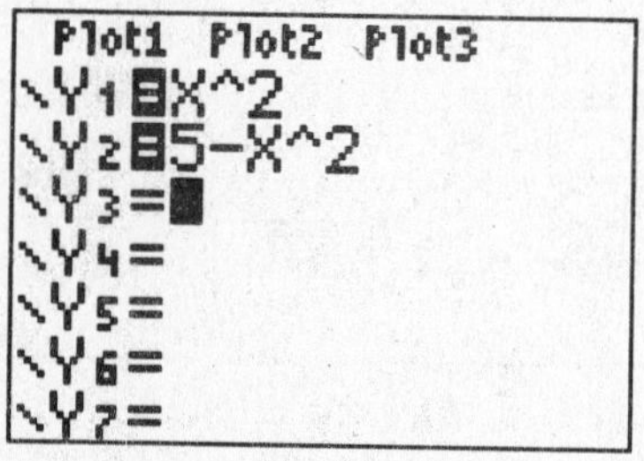

Figure 2.45: *Displaying the graphs of two functions*

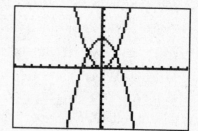

Which graph is which? We can use $\boxed{\text{TRACE}}$ to help us keep track of which graph goes with which function. When we do this with the TI-83, we see in Figure 2.46 that the formula for the graph the cursor is on shows in the upper-left corner of the screen. (On the TI-82 a 1 will appear in the upper-right corner indicating that this is the graph of Y_1.) If we use $\boxed{\triangle}$ or $\boxed{\nabla}$, the cursor switches to the other graph, and as we see in Figure 2.47, the corresponding function is shown in the upper left corner of the screen. (On the TI-82 a 2 will appear in the upper right corner indicating that this is the graph of Y_2.)

Figure 2.46: How TRACE *labels graphs on the TI-83*

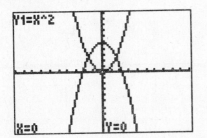

Figure 2.47: Using △ *to move to the next graph*

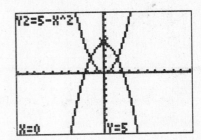

Changing the look of the graph on the TI-83: The TI-83 allows the display to show different graphs in different styles, providing additional help in keeping track of which graph is which. (This feature is not available on the TI-82.) Let's change the look of the graph of $5 - x^2$. Use $Y =$ and move the highlight to the left of $Y_2=$ and press ENTER . This will cause the slash displayed there to start blinking. Now if we press ENTER , its shape will change as shown in Figure 2.48. (If you press ENTER more times, you will cycle through several display options.) Now when we GRAPH , the graph of $5 - x^2$ is shown with a heavy line as in Figure 2.49.

Figure 2.48: Changing the graphing tag on the TI-83

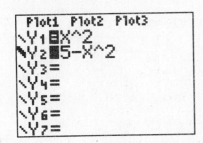

Figure 2.49: $5 - x^2$ shown with a heavy line on the TI-83

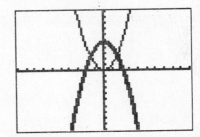

Turning off graph displays: There may be occasions when we want to show one graph but not erase the other function from the function entry screen. Let's show how to turn off the display of the graph of x^2 without erasing its formula. Use $Y =$ to return to the function entry screen. Notice that the equal sign on both the Y_1 and Y_2 lines are highlighted. Move the cursor to the equal sign on the Y_1 line and press ENTER . This will turn off the highlight as shown in Figure 2.50. Now when we GRAPH as in Figure 2.51, only the graphs of functions with highlighted equal signs will be displayed. To turn the display back on, use $Y =$, move the highlight to the equal sign, and press ENTER again.

Figure 2.50: Turning off the highlight on =

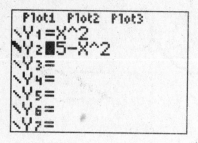

Figure 2.51: Graph with x^2 turned off

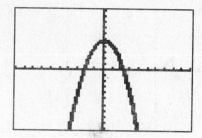

CHAPTER 2: SOLVING EQUATIONS USING THE CROSSING GRAPHS METHOD

Let's show how to use the graphing capabilities of the calculator to solve

$$\frac{x^3}{10} + x = 5 - \frac{x^2}{2} \tag{2.1}$$

using what the text refers to as *the crossing graphs method*. We want to graph each side of Equation (2.1) and see where they are the same; that is where the graphs cross. The first step is to enter the left-hand side of the equation as one function and the right-hand side as a second function. Use $\boxed{Y =}$ and $\boxed{\text{CLEAR}}$ out old functions. On the $Y_1 =$ line enter $\boxed{X, T, \Theta, n}$ $\boxed{\wedge}$ 3 $\boxed{\div}$ 10 $\boxed{+}$ $\boxed{X, T, \Theta, n}$, and on the $Y_2 =$ line enter 5 $\boxed{-}$ $\boxed{X, T, \Theta, n}$ $\boxed{\wedge}$ 2 $\boxed{\div}$ 2 . The correctly entered functions are in Figure 2.52. Use $\boxed{\text{ZOOM}}$ 6 to get the ZStandard view of the graphs shown in the Figure 2.53. Note that we have used $\boxed{\text{TRACE}}$ to show which graph goes with which function. The point in Figure 2.53 where the graphs cross is where the left-hand and right-hand sides of the equation are the same. To solve Equation (2.1), we want the X-value of that crossing point.

To locate the crossing point we first press $\boxed{\text{2nd}}$ [CALC] to get the CALCULATE menu shown in Figure 2.54. We want to know where the graphs cross, so we choose 5:intersect from the menu. The calculator will return you to the graphing screen with the prompt First curve? at the bottom of the screen. Press $\boxed{\text{ENTER}}$ and you will see the prompt Second curve?. Press $\boxed{\text{ENTER}}$ again. You will now see the graph with Guess? at the bottom. Press $\boxed{\text{ENTER}}$ a final time, and Intersection will appear at the bottom of the screen together with the coordinates of the crossing point. From Figure 2.55 we see that the graphs cross when $x = 2.0470371$, and so, rounding to two decimal places, we report the solution to Equation (2.1) as $x = 2.05$.

Figure 2.52: Entering $\frac{x^3}{10} + x$ *and* $5 - \frac{x^2}{2}$

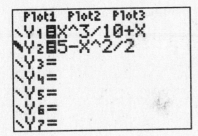

Figure 2.53: The graphs of $\frac{x^3}{10} + x$ *and* $5 - \frac{x^2}{2}$

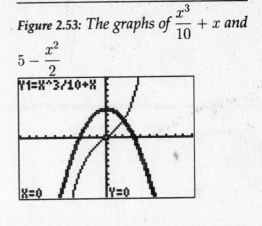

Figure 2.54: The **CALCULATE** *menu*

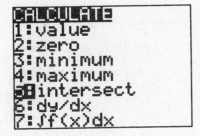

Figure 2.55: Solving with the crossing graphs method

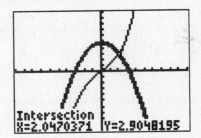

Briefly, to solve with the crossing graphs method, you use $\boxed{Y=}$ and enter each side of the equation on a separate line. Then $\boxed{\text{GRAPH}}$ and make necessary adjustments so that the crossing point is shown. Press $\boxed{\text{2nd}}$ [CALC] and select 5:intersect from the menu. In general you can get the intersection point from here by pressing $\boxed{\text{ENTER}}$ three times. The intermediate prompts **First curve?** and **Second curve?** are there in case you have more than two graphs on the screen. The prompt **Guess?** is there in case more than one crossing point is on the screen. In that case, move the cursor near the crossing point you want before pressing $\boxed{\text{ENTER}}$. You may also have to move the cursor near the crossing point you want on the rare occasion that the sequence 5:intersect $\boxed{\text{ENTER}}$ $\boxed{\text{ENTER}}$ $\boxed{\text{ENTER}}$ fails to produce an answer. Finally, you should be aware that for this method to work the crossing point you want must appear in the graphing window.

CHAPTER 2: SOLVING EQUATIONS USING THE SINGLE GRAPH METHOD

We will show an alternative way, which we will refer to as *the single graph method*, for solving Equation (2.1). First we move everything from the right-hand side of the equation over to the left-hand side, remembering to change the sign of each term:

$$\frac{x^3}{10} + x = 5 - \frac{x^2}{2} \tag{2.2}$$

$$\frac{x^3}{10} + x - 5 + \frac{x^2}{2} = 0. \tag{2.3}$$

Now use $\boxed{Y=}$ and $\boxed{\text{CLEAR}}$ the old functions before entering

$$\boxed{X,T,\Theta,n} \; \boxed{\wedge} \; 3 \; \boxed{\div} \; 10 \; \boxed{+} \; \boxed{X,T,\Theta,n}$$
$$\boxed{-} \; 5 \; \boxed{+} \; \boxed{X,T,\Theta,n} \; \boxed{\wedge} \; 2 \; \boxed{\div} \; 2$$

as shown in Figure 2.56. Use $\boxed{\text{ZOOM}}$ 6 to get the ZStandard view shown Figure 2.57. The solution of Equation (2.3) is where the graph crosses the horizontal axis. This point is referred to as a *root* or *zero*. The TI-82 uses *root* while the TI-83 uses *zero*. We will adhere to the TI-83 convention, and refer to it as a zero.

Figure 2.56: Entering the function in preparation for the single graph method

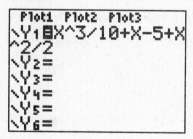

Figure 2.57: The root or zero

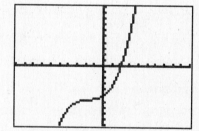

To find this point press $\boxed{\text{2nd}}$ [CALC] , but this time from the **CALCULATE** menu, we select **2:zero** (or **2:root** on the TI-82) as shown in Figure 2.58. The graphing screen will appear once more with the prompt **Left Bound?** (or **Lower Bound?** on the TI-82) at the bottom as shown in Figure 2.59.

The calculator is asking for help to obtain the solution. We provide it by using $\boxed{\triangleleft}$ to move the cursor to any point to the left of the zero and pressing $\boxed{\text{ENTER}}$. We are presented with Figure 2.60, where our selection is marked at the top of the screen, and at the bottom we see the new prompt **Right Bound?** (or **Upper Bound?** on the TI-82). This time we use $\boxed{\triangleright}$ to

Figure 2.58: The CALCULATE *menu with* 2:zero *highlighted*

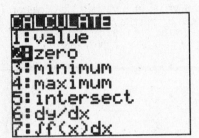

Figure 2.59: *Prompting for the* Left Bound

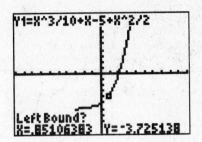

move the cursor to the right of the zero and press $\boxed{\text{ENTER}}$ again. We see in Figure 2.61 that there are now two marks at the top of the screen and a Guess? prompt at the bottom. The

Figure 2.60: *The left bound marked and the* Right Bound? *prompt*

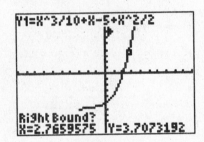

Figure 2.61: *Both bounds marked and the* Guess? *prompt*

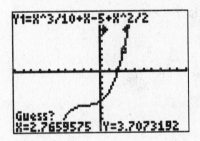

crossing point must be between the displayed marks. We respond to the Guess? prompt by pressing $\boxed{\text{ENTER}}$, and we see the solution $x = 2.0470371$ to Equation (2.3) in Figure 2.62. As we expected, this agrees with the answer we got using the crossing graphs method.

Figure 2.62: *The solution of* $\dfrac{x^3}{11} + x - 5 + \dfrac{x^2}{2} = 0$ *using the single graph method*

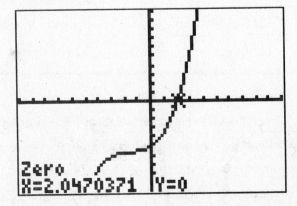

As with the crossing graphs method, there are a couple of things that should be noted. Be sure the zero you want actually appears in the graphing window, and that there is only one in the range from the **Left Bound** to the **Right Bound** that you provide. On the rare occasion when you do not get an answer, you may need to move the bounds closer, or at the **Guess?** prompt move the cursor as near the root as you can.

CHAPTER 2: OPTIMIZATION

Maxima and *minima* or *peaks* and *valleys* of a graph can be located on the TI-82/83 in much the same way that roots or zeros are found. To illustrate the method, we will look at the graph of

$$f = 2^x - x^2 .$$

Use $\boxed{Y=}$, $\boxed{\text{CLEAR}}$ out any old functions from the list, and enter the new one using

2 $\boxed{\wedge}$ $\boxed{X,T,\Theta,n}$ $\boxed{-}$ $\boxed{X,T,\Theta,n}$ $\boxed{\wedge}$ 2 . The graph of the function shown in Figure 2.63 uses **Xmin=** $\boxed{(-)}$ 1 , **Xmax=4** , **Ymin=** $\boxed{(-)}$ 2 , and **Ymax=2** .

Figure 2.63: The graph of $2^x - x^2$

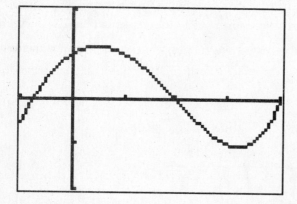

The graph in Figure 2.63 shows a maximum, or a peak, and a minimum, or a valley. The keystrokes required to find them are very similar, but we will carefully find both. Let's first find the maximum. Press $\boxed{\text{2nd}}$ [CALC] to get to the **CALCULATE** menu shown in Figure 2.64. We want to find the maximum, so we select **4:maximum** from the menu. We are returned to the graphing window with the trace option turned on, and the prompt **Left Bound?** (or **Lower bound?** on the TI-82) appears at the bottom of the screen as in Figure 2.65. The in-

Figure 2.64: *Selecting* 4:maximum *from the* CALCULATE *menu*

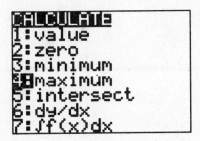

Figure 2.65: The Left Bound? *prompt*

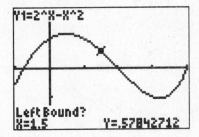

formation wanted now by the calculator is similar to what is wanted when we search for zeros or roots. We use the arrow keys to move the cursor to the left of the maximum and press ENTER . A tick mark is placed at the top of the screen showing our selection, and we see the Right Bound? (or Upper bound? on the TI-82) prompt in Figure 2.66. We move the cursor to the right of the maximum and press ENTER again. Now we see two tick marks at the top of the screen *which must enclose the maximum we want* and the Guess? prompt in Figure 2.67. Rarely is any response other than ENTER required here, and the maximum will be located

Figure 2.66: The Right Bound? *prompt*

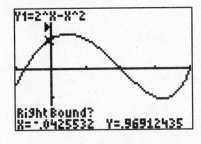

Figure 2.67: The Guess? *prompt*

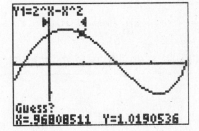

as in Figure 2.68.

The steps for finding the minimum are almost identical with those we used to get the maximum. Press 2nd [CALC] , but this time select 3:minimum from the menu as shown in Figure 2.69. As with the maximum we are returned to the graphing window with the trace option on and the Left Bound? prompt showing in Figure 2.70. We locate the cursor left of the minimum and press ENTER , move the cursor to the right of the minimum and press ENTER , and finally press ENTER at the Guess? prompt. The minimum will be found as in Figure 2.71.

We should note that on the rare occasion when the method described here fails to pro-

Figure 2.68: Locating a maximum for $2^x - x^2$

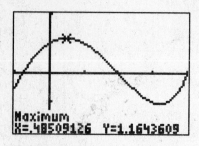

Figure 2.69: Selecting 3:minimum from the CALCULATE menu

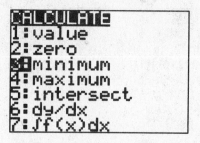

Figure 2.70: The Left Bound? *prompt for the minimum*

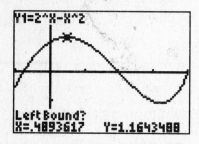

Figure 2.71: A minimum value for $2^x - x^2$

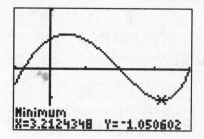

duce the desired result, you should repeat the procedure, but at the Guess? prompt, move the cursor as near the maximum or minimum as you can and press ⎡ENTER⎤ .

CHAPTER 2: GRAPHICS CONFIGURATION NOTES

There are a number of ways your calculator can be configured to display graphics. If you were able to follow the examples in the earlier section entitled Chapter 2: Graphs, reproducing the screens we made, then you won't need to use these notes. If not, the difficulty may be that your calculator graphics configuration has been altered from the factory set defaults. These notes address only the two most common graphics settings which may have been changed on your calculator. If this does not solve your graphics configuration difficulties, consult your calculator manual.

Problem: *My graphs match those in the examples until I zoom in or out. Then I get a different picture.* The probable cause is that the default zoom factors have been changed. To find out and fix the problem, press ⎡ZOOM⎤ and use ⎡▷⎤ to highlight MEMORY as shown in Figure 2.72. Select 4:Set Factors from the menu. This will take you to the ZOOM FACTORS menu shown in Figure 2.73. Your screen should show XFact=4 and YFact=4. If necessary, change these numbers to match Figure 2.73.

Figure 2.72: *The* ZOOM MEMORY *menu*

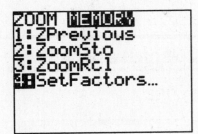

Figure 2.73: *The* ZOOM FACTORS *menu*

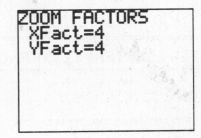

Problem: *When I* GRAPH *, I get an error as in Figure 2.74, or I get the graphs, but I also get some extra dots as in Figure 2.75 or some dots connected by lines as in Figure 2.76. The probable*

Figure 2.74: *Error reported when you* GRAPH

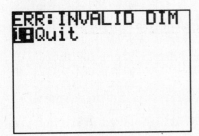

Figure 2.75: *Discrete statistical plot turned on*

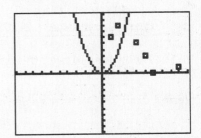

cause is that you have one form or another of statistical plotting turned on. To correct this problem press 2nd [STAT PLOT] to get to the STAT PLOTS menu shown in Figure 2.77. We want to turn statistical plotting Off, so we press 4 and then ENTER .

Figure 2.76: *Connected statistical plot turned on*

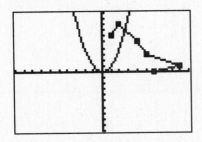

Figure 2.77: *The* STAT PLOTS *menu*

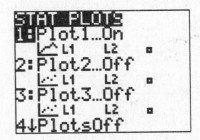

Discrete Data

The TI-82/83 offers many features for handling discrete data sets. This chapter shows how to enter data and perform some basic analysis.

CHAPTER 3: ENTERING, EDITING AND GRAPHING DISCRETE DATA

Many times information about physical or social phenomena is obtained by gathering individual bits of data and recording it in a table. For example, the following table taken from the 1996 *Information Please Almanac* shows median American family income I by year in terms of 1996 dollars. That means the dollar amounts shown have been adjusted to account for inflation. The variable d in the table is years since 1980. Thus, for example, the $d = 2$ column corresponds to 1982.

d = years since 1980	0	1	2	3	4	5
I = median income	21,023	22,388	23,433	24,580	26,433	27,735

Let's show how to enter this data into the calculator and display it graphically.

Entering data: To enter the values from the table above, we press $\boxed{\text{STAT}}$ to get the EDIT CALC TESTS menu shown in Figure 2.78. Be sure EDIT is highlighted. If it is not, use $\boxed{◁}$ to change that. Choose 1:Edit, and you will see a screen similar to the one in Figure 2.79. Figure 2.79 shows that our calculator has some old data already entered, and

---

Figure 2.78: *Using* $\boxed{\text{STAT}}$ *to get the* EDIT CALC TESTS *menu*

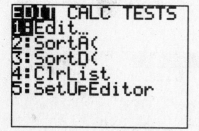

Figure 2.79: *The data entry screen with old data*

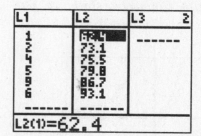

---

we need to clear it out before entering new data. Use $\boxed{△}$ to highlight L1 as shown in Figure 2.79 and then press $\boxed{\text{CLEAR}}$ $\boxed{\text{ENTER}}$. Do the same with each column that has unwanted entries. You should now have the clear data entry screen shown in Figure 2.80. The L1 column corresponds to d, and we type in the d values 0 through 5, pressing either $\boxed{\text{ENTER}}$ or $\boxed{\triangledown}$ after each entry. Now use $\boxed{\triangleright}$ to move to the top of the L2 column and enter the median incomes there. The completed data entry is in Figure 2.81.

Figure 2.80: A fresh data entry screen

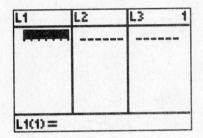

Figure 2.81: Completed data entry

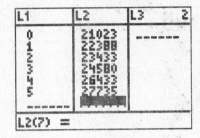

Turning on (or off) statistical plots: Before we can make of graphical display of data, we need to set up the calculator so that it can display discrete data. That is, we must turn on statistical plotting. This only has to be done the first time we want to make such a picture (or if we ourselves have disabled this feature). Once turned on, the statistical plotting will stay on until we turn it off. To set up statistical plotting, press $\boxed{\text{2nd}}$ [STAT PLOT] to get the menu shown in Figure 2.82. Select 1:Plot 1 from that menu, and the TI-83 will present you with the menu in Figure 2.83. The menu for the TI-82 is similar. Highlight

Figure 2.82: The STAT PLOTS menu

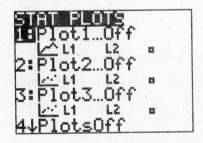

Figure 2.83: The Plot 1 menu

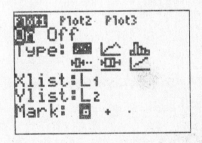

On and press $\boxed{\text{ENTER}}$. Your screen should now match the one in Figure 2.83. Check the Type:, Xlist, Ylist, and Mark lines to see that they agree with Figure 2.83. If they do not, use the arrow keys to move the highlight where you want it, change the entry, and press $\boxed{\text{ENTER}}$. When you no longer want data points to appear in your graphs, you can repeat this procedure, turning Plot 1 Off.

It is particularly important to note the role of the Xlist and Ylist lines in Figure 2.83. The

Xlist line determines which of the data columns will be shown on the horizontal axis. Usually, this is L1. To set it on the TI-83, use $\boxed{\text{2nd}}$ [L1] (above the 1 key); on the TI-82, highlight L1 and press $\boxed{\text{ENTER}}$. The Ylist line determines which of the data columns will be shown on the vertical axis. Usually, this is L2, which you set on the TI-83 by using $\boxed{\text{2nd}}$ [L2] (above the 2 key) and on the TI-82 by highlighting L2 and pressing $\boxed{\text{ENTER}}$.

Plotting the data: Now we are ready to view the graph. Generally with discrete data, we don't have to worry with how to set up the window, because the TI-82/83 has a special feature which does the job automatically. This feature is accessed as follows. Press $\boxed{\text{ZOOM}}$, and move down the ZOOM menu to 9:ZoomStat as shown in Figure 2.84. When you press 9 (or $\boxed{\text{ENTER}}$ with 9:ZoomStat highlighted) you will see the graphical display in Figure 2.85. If you got the picture in Figure 2.85 with one or more extra graphs added, you need to use $\boxed{Y=}$ and clear out any old functions that are on the function entry screen.

Figure 2.84: The ZoomStat *option*

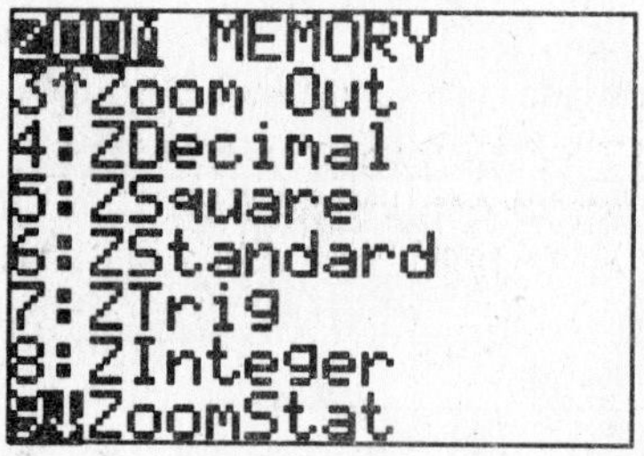

Figure 2.85: Displaying median income data

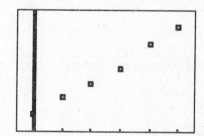

When you use ZoomStat to display data, the calculator decides the window size to use. You can see what its choices were by pressing $\boxed{\text{WINDOW}}$. We see in Figure 2.86 that the horizontal span is -0.5 to 5.5 and the vertical span is from 19,881.96 to 28,876.04.

Adding regular graphs to data plots: You can add any graph you wish to a data plot. For example, using a technique known as *linear regression*, which is discussed in the text *Functions and Change* and is reviewed in the next section of this guide, we find that the linear function $y = 1338x + 20919$ closely approximates the median income data. To show its graph, use $\boxed{Y=}$, type 1338 $\boxed{X,T,\Theta,n}$ $\boxed{+}$ 20919, and then $\boxed{\text{GRAPH}}$. This line added to the data plot is in Figure 2.87.

Editing columns: There are shortcuts that make it easy to do certain kinds of data edits. For example, suppose we wish to show median income remaining after each family pays a

Figure 2.86: The window size selected by ZoomStat

```
WINDOW
 Xmin=1.5
 Xmax=5.5
 Xscl=1
 Ymin=19881.96
 Ymax=28876.04
 Yscl=1
 Xres=1
```

Figure 2.87: Adding an additional graph

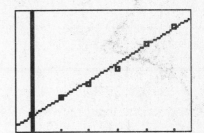

17% tax. That is, we want to replace each entry in the L2 column by 83% of its current value. Use $\boxed{\text{STAT}}$ and choose 1:**Edit** from the menu to get to the data we have already entered. Use the arrow keys to highlight L3 as shown in Figure 2.88. We want to put in the L3 column the entries in the L2 column times 0.83. We could calculate these values one at a time and enter each individually, but the TI-82/83 offers a much easier way to accomplish this. Just type . 83 $\boxed{\text{2nd}}$ [L2] as seen at the bottom of the screen in Figure 2.89. Now when we press $\boxed{\text{ENTER}}$, the L3 column is filled in automatically as in Figure 2.90.

Figure 2.88: Preparing for entry in the L3 *column*

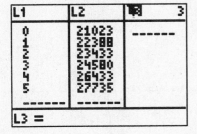

Figure 2.89: The formula entered

```
L1        L2        L3        3
0         21023     ------
1         22300
2         23433
3         24500
4         26433
5         27735
------    ------
L3 =.83L2
```

Let's show how to plot this new data. Now we want the L1 column on the horizontal axis, but the L3 column rather than the L2 column for the vertical axis. To make this happen, use $\boxed{\text{2nd}}$ [STAT PLOT] and select 1:**Plot1** from the menu. Go to the **Ylist:** line and type $\boxed{\text{2nd}}$ [L3] (on the TI-82, highlight L3 and press $\boxed{\text{ENTER}}$) as shown in Figure 2.91. Now when we $\boxed{\text{ZOOM}}$ 9 we see the new data displayed in Figure 2.92. (Don't forget to use $\boxed{Y =}$ and clear out the Y_1 line, which we don't want to see anymore.)

Figure 2.90: *The* L3 *column filled auto-matically*

L1	L2	L3	3
0	21023	**17449**	
1	22388	18582	
2	23433	19449	
3	24580	20401	
4	26433	21939	
5	27735	23020	
-----	-----	-----	

L3(1)=17449.09

Figure 2.91: *Changing the vertical axis from* L2 *to* L3

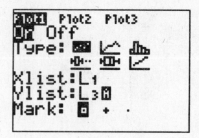

Figure 2.92: *Data after 17% tax*

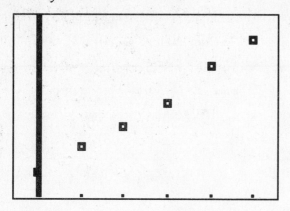

CHAPTER 3: LINEAR REGRESSION

Linear regression is a method of getting a linear function which approximates almost linear data. The TI-82/83 has built-in features which will do this automatically. Let's show how to do it for the following data table.

x	0	1	2	3	4
y	17	19.3	20.9	22.7	26.1

The first step is to enter the data. This is done exactly as described in the previous section. Use $\boxed{\text{STAT}}$ and select 1:Edit from the menu. $\boxed{\text{CLEAR}}$ out old data as necessary to get the clear data entry screen in Figure 2.93. Next enter the x data in the L1 column and the y data in the L2 column as shown in Figure 2.94.

To get the regression line press $\boxed{\text{STAT}}$ and use $\boxed{\triangleright}$ to move the highlight at the top

Figure 2.93: *A clear data entry screen*

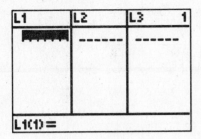

Figure 2.94: *The correctly entered data*

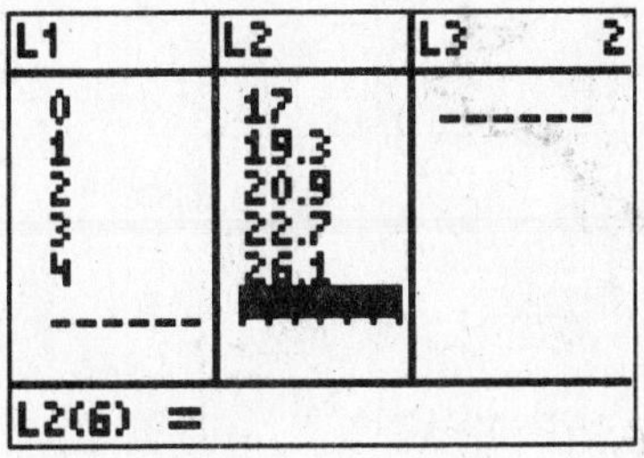

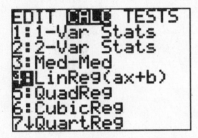

of the screen to CALC. This will change the menu to the one shown in Figure 2.95. From this menu select 4:LinReg(ax+b) (this is 5:LinReg(ax+b) on the TI-82). You will be taken to the calculation screen with LinReg(ax+b) displayed as shown in Figure 2.96. Press $\boxed{\text{ENTER}}$, and

Figure 2.95: *The statistical calculation menu* (LinReg(ax+b) *is menu item* 5 *on the TI-82.)*

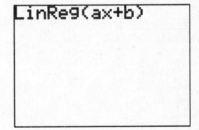

Figure 2.96: *The regression line prompt*

you will see the information in Figure 2.97. (The TI-82 displays an additional line, which we will not use.)

This screen tells us that the equation of the regression line is $y = ax + b$, where the slope is $a = 2.16$, and the vertical intercept is $b = 16.88$. (Note here that the TI-82/83 uses a for the slope rather than the more familiar m.) Thus the equation of the regression line is $y = 2.16x + 16.88$.

We have in fact completed the calculation of the regression line, but it is almost always important to continue and make a display of the data and the regression line together. Among other things, such a display provides a valuable check for our work. To graph the line, we must get the regression line formula into the function entry screen. We will first show how to do this manually and then later show a method for having it automatically entered in the function list at the time it is calculated. For manual entry use $\boxed{Y=}$, $\boxed{\text{CLEAR}}$ out old functions, and type the equation of the regression line as 2 . 16 $\boxed{X, T, \Theta, n}$ $\boxed{+}$ 16 . 88 . The correctly entered function is in Figure 2.98.

Figure 2.97: *Regression line parameters*

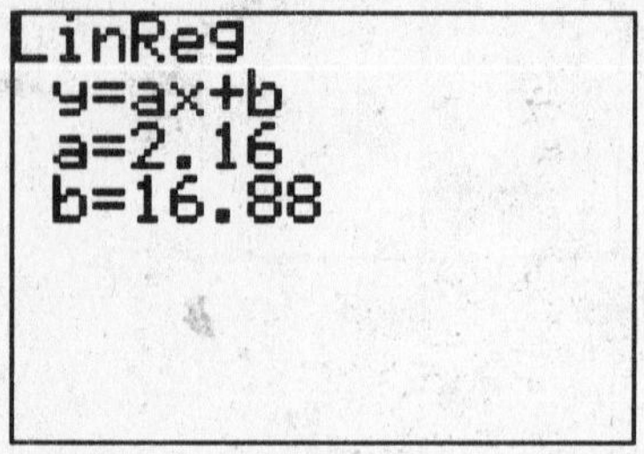

```
LinReg
 y=ax+b
 a=2.16
 b=16.88
```

Figure 2.98: *Manual entry of the regression line formula*

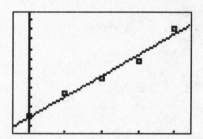

Before we make the graph, we use   2nd   [STAT PLOT] and check to see that **Plot1** is configured as in Figure 2.99. Finally   ZOOM   9   produces the picture in Figure 2.100.

Figure 2.99: *The properly configured* **Plot1** *window*

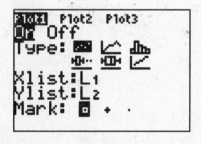

Figure 2.100: *Data and regression line*

The important feature to note in Figure 2.100 is that the regression line closely approximates the data points. If this does not happen, we know either that we have made a mistake, or that the data is not properly modeled using a linear function.

Automatic entry of the regression line on the function list: Let's calculate the regression line again, this time showing how to make it automatically appear on the function list. This method is available only on the TI-83.[4] Just as before, we use   STAT , select the **CALC** menu, and choose 4: **LinReg(ax+b)**. Now at the regression line prompt shown in Figure 2.96 above, press   VARS   and highlight **Y-VARS** at the top of the screen to see the *y*-variables menu. Be sure that 1:**Function** is highlighted in that menu as shown in Figure 2.101. Now when you

---

[4]There is another method for transferring the equation of the regression line to the function entry screen without typing it, a method that is available on both calculators. Use   Y = ,   CLEAR   the Y₁= line, and then press   VARS . Select 5:**Statistics**. Move the highlight at the top of the screen to EQ and then choose 1:**RegEQ** (on the TI-82 this is 7:**RegEQ**) from the menu.

press ENTER , you will be presented with the list in Figure 2.102. Be sure 1:Y1 is highlighted

---

Figure 2.101: *The y-variables menu*

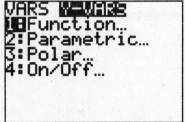

Figure 2.102: *Function list*

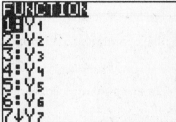

and press ENTER . You will be returned to the home screen with Y1 added to the regression prompt, as seen in Figure 2.103. Now when you press ENTER , the regression line parameters will be calculated as usual, but also the regression line formula will appear on the function list. In Figure 2.104 we have pressed $Y =$ to verify that this has occurred.

Figure 2.103: *Completing the regression prompt*

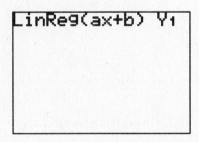

Figure 2.104: *Regression formula automatically entered*

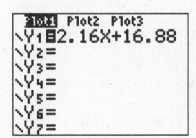

We should note that this is a case where the explanation is so long that it may appear to make the procedure more complicated than it really is. If you go through the keystrokes a few times, you may find this quick and easy indeed. This procedure is available to you, and manual function entry is also available. You should choose the method that seems best to you.

CHAPTER 4: EXPONENTIAL REGRESSION

The logarithm can be used to transform exponential or power data into linear data and thus allow us to get an appropriate model using linear regression. To transform exponential data, we take the logarithm of function values, leaving input values as they are. For power data, the logarithm of both input values and function values is taken.

To make an exponential model for data such as

input values	a	b	...
function values	z	w	...

we apply the logarithm to the function values to produce new data

input values	a	b	...
function values	$\ln z$	$\ln w$	...

Next we get the regression line $y = mx + b$ for this transformed data. The exponential model we want is then $e^b \times (e^m)^x$. The alternative form for the model (described in Section 4.4 of *Functions and Change*) is $e^b e^{mx}$.

We can illustrate the method by getting an exponential model for the data in the following table:

x	1	2	3	4	5
y	0.55	0.83	1.5	2.7	4.4

The first step is to use $\boxed{\text{STAT}}$ and 1:Edit to enter the data as shown in Figure 2.105. It will prove convenient if we enter the data in columns 1 and 3, leaving column 2 blank for now. To transform the data, we highlight the L2 at the top of the second column and enter $\boxed{\text{LN}}$ $\boxed{\text{2nd}}$ [L3] (on the TI-83 this is followed by $\boxed{)}$) as shown in Figure 2.106. Now when we press $\boxed{\text{ENTER}}$, the L2 column will be automatically filled with the logarithm of the data as seen in Figure 2.107. Now we get the regression line as usual using $\boxed{\text{STAT}}$ CALC 4:LinReg(ax+b) (this is 5:LinReg(ax+b) on the TI-82). We have edited the regression line prompt using $\boxed{\text{VARS}}$ Y-VARS 1:Function Y1, as shown in Figure 2.103 above, so that the regression line formula will be automatically put on the function list. From Figure 2.108 we see that the regression line formula, with rounding to three decimal places, is $0.534x - 1.182$.

Figure 2.105: *Correctly entered data*

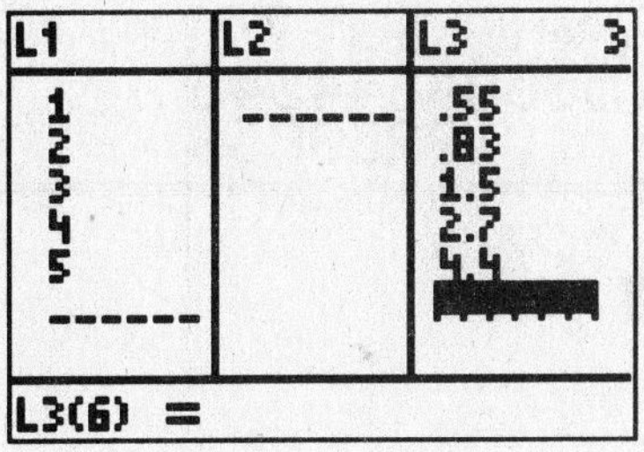

Figure 2.106: *Preparing to transform the data*

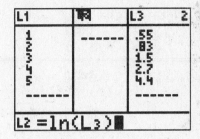

Figure 2.107: *The L2 column filled automatically*

Figure 2.108: *Regression line paramters*

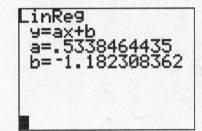

The needed exponential model in the alternative form is then $e^{-1.182}e^{0.534x} = 0.31e^{0.534x}$. Since $e^{0.534} = 1.71$, we can write the standard form as 0.31×1.71^x. We want now to use the calculator to display the original data along with the exponential model we have made. We use $\boxed{Y=}$, and manually enter the exponential model in the alternative form on the Y2= line as shown in Figure 2.109. As with the regression line, there is a different way of entering the exponential model. You may or may not find it more convenient than manual entry. For the TI-83, on the Y2= line type $\boxed{2\text{nd}}$ [e^x] $\boxed{\text{VARS}}$ Y-VARS 1:Function 1:Y1, followed by $\boxed{)}$. For the TI-82, on the Y2= line type $\boxed{2\text{nd}}$ [e^x] $\boxed{2\text{nd}}$ [Y-VARS] 1:Function 1:Y1. This different entry method is shown in Figure 2.110.

Note that both in Figure 2.109 and in Figure 2.110 we have removed the highlight from the = sign on the Y1 line (by moving the cursor to the equal sign and pressing $\boxed{\text{ENTER}}$) so that function will not be graphed. Before graphing, it is important that we graph the original data that we put in columns 1 and 3 of the data list. To make sure, we use $\boxed{2\text{nd}}$ [STAT PLOT] 1:Plot 1, and make sure Xlist is set to L1 and Ylist is set to L3. The properly configured menu is in Figure 2.111. Now we $\boxed{\text{ZOOM}}$ 9 , and the data along with the exponential model appear as in Figure 2.112.

Figure 2.109: Manual entry of the exponential model

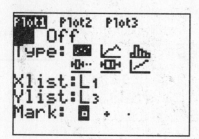

Figure 2.110: Alternative method of entering exponential model

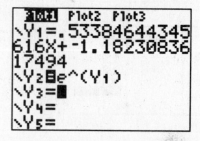

Figure 2.111: The properly configured Stat Plot menu

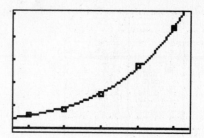

Figure 2.112: The data along with the exponential model

CHAPTER 5: POWER REGRESSION

Power models can be constructed in much the same way as exponential models. The key difference is that we apply the logarithm to both input values and function values.

To make a power model for data such as

input values	a	b	...
function values	z	w	...

we apply the logarithm to produce new data

input values	$\ln a$	$\ln b$	...
function values	$\ln z$	$\ln w$	...

Next we get the regression line $y = mx + b$ for this transformed data. The power model we want is then $e^b x^m$.

We illustrate the method by getting a power model for the following data:

x	1	2	3	4	5
y	0.22	0.54	0.88	1.25	1.91

We use $\boxed{\text{STAT}}$ 1:Edit and enter the data in columns L3 and L4 as shown in Figure 2.113. We want the logarithm of the L3 data in column L1, so we highlight L1 and $\boxed{\text{LN}}$ $\boxed{\text{2nd}}$ [L3] (followed by $\boxed{)}$ on the TI-83). Next highlight L2 and type $\boxed{\text{LN}}$ $\boxed{\text{2nd}}$ [L4] (followed by $\boxed{)}$ on the TI-83). The completed data entry is shown in Figure 2.114.

Figure 2.113: *Entering the data*

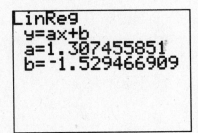

Figure 2.114: *Applying the logarithm*

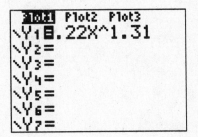

Now we can get the regression line parameters using $\boxed{\text{STAT}}$ CALC 4:LinReg(ax+b) (this is 5:LinReg(ax+b) on the TI-82). We see from Figure 2.115 that the regression line formula is $1.31x - 1.529$. Since $e^{-1.529} = 0.22$, the appropriate power model is $0.22x^{1.31}$. In Figure 2.116 we have entered this on the function list.

Figure 2.115: *Regression line parameters*

```
LinReg
y=ax+b
a=1.307455851
b=-1.529466909
```

Figure 2.116: *Entering the power model*

```
Plot1 Plot2 Plot3
\Y1■.22X^1.31
\Y2=
\Y3=
\Y4=
\Y5=
\Y6=
\Y7=
```

Our original data is in columns L3 and L4, so we use $\boxed{\text{2nd}}$ [STAT PLOT] and check that Xlist is set to L3 and Ylist is set to L4, as shown in Figure 2.117. Now if we $\boxed{\text{ZOOM}}$ 9 , the original data along with the power model will appear as in Figure 2.118.

Figure 2.117: Properly configured Xlist *and* Ylist

Figure 2.118: Data with power model

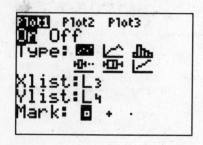

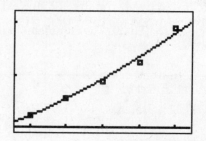

PART III *Drill Exercises*

Drill exercises for the Prologue

1. **Basic calculations:** $\dfrac{2.6 \times 5.9}{6.3}$

2. **Basic calculations:** $3^{3.2} - 2^{2.3}$

3. **Basic calculations:** $\dfrac{e}{\sqrt{\pi}}$

4. **Basic calculations:** $\dfrac{7.6^{1.7}}{9.2}$

5. **Parentheses and grouping:** $\dfrac{7.3 - 6.8}{2.5 + 1.8}$

6. **Parentheses and grouping:** $3^{2.4 \times 1.8 - 2}$

7. **Parentheses and grouping:** $\dfrac{\sqrt{6 + e} + 1}{3}$

8. **Parentheses and grouping:** $\dfrac{\pi - e}{\pi + e}$

9. **Subtraction versus sign:** $\dfrac{-3}{4 - 9}$

10. **Subtraction versus sign:** $-2 - 4^{-3}$

11. **Subtraction versus sign:** $-\sqrt{8.6 - 3.9}$

12. **Subtraction versus sign:** $\dfrac{-\sqrt{10} + 5^{-0.3}}{17 - 6.6}$

13. **Chain calculations:** All of the following can be done with a single entry, but they are intended to provide practice with chain calculations.

    (a) $\dfrac{3}{7.2 + 5.9} + \dfrac{7}{6.4 \times 2.8}$

    (b) $\left(1 + \dfrac{1}{36}\right)^{\left(1 - \frac{1}{36}\right)}$

14. **Scientific notation:** The following numbers are written in scientific notation. Express them as ordinary decimals.

   (a) 3.62×10^4

   (b) 7.19×10^6

   (c) 3.13×10^{-3}

   (d) 4.67×10^{-7}

Drill exercises for Section 1.1

1. **Evaluating formulas:** Evaluate $f(x) = \dfrac{\sqrt{x+1}}{x^2+1}$ at $x = 2$.

2. **Evaluating formulas:** Evaluate $f(x) = \left(3 + x^{1.2}\right)^{x+3.8}$ at $x = 4.3$.

3. **Evaluating formulas:** Evaluate $g(x,y) = \dfrac{x^3 + y^3}{x^2 + y^2}$ at $x = 4.1, y = 2.6$.

4. **Getting function values:** If $f(t) = 87.1 - e^{4t}$, calculate $f(1.3)$.

5. **Getting function values:** If $f(s) = \dfrac{s^2 + 1}{s^2 - 1}$, calculate $f(6.1)$.

6. **Evaluating functions of several variables:** If $f(r,s,t) = \sqrt{r + \sqrt{s + \sqrt{t}}}$, calculate $f(2,5,7)$.

7. **Evaluating functions of several variables:** If $h(x,y,z) = \dfrac{x^y}{z}$, calculate $f(3, 2.2, 9.7)$.

8. **Using formulas:** If $p(t)$ is the profit I expect my business to earn t years after opening, use functional notation to express expected profit after two years and six months.

9. **Using formulas:** If $c(p, s, h)$ is the cost of buying p bags of potato chips, s sodas, and h hot dogs, use functional notation to express the cost of buying two bags of chips, 3 sodas, and 5 hot dogs.

10. **What formulas mean:** If $s(L)$ is the top speed in miles per hour of a fish that is L inches long, what does $s(13)$ mean?

Drill exercises for Section 1.2

1. **A tabulated function:** The following table gives values for a function $N = N(t)$.

t	10	20	30	40	50	60	70
$N = N(t)$	17.6	23.8	44.6	51.3	53.2	53.7	53.9

Find the value of $N(20)$.

2. **Averaging:** Using the table in Exercise 1, estimate the value of $N(25)$ by averaging.

3. **Average rate of change:** Using the table from Exercise 1, what is the average rate of change in N from $t = 20$ to $t = 30$?

4. **Using average rates of change:** Use your answer in Exercise 3 to estimate the value of $N(23)$.

5. **Averaging:** Using the table in Exercise 1, estimate the value of $N(35)$ by averaging.

6. **Average rate of change:** Using the table from Exercise 1, what is the average rate of change in N from $t = 30$ to $t = 40$?

7. **Using average rates of change:** Use your answer from the exercise above estimate the value of $N(37)$.

8. **Limiting values:** Assuming the function N in Exercise 1 describes a physical situation for which a limiting value is expected, estimate the limiting value of N.

9. **When limiting values occur:** Suppose $c(t)$ represents the number of cars your dealership sells in year t. If your car dealership sells almost exclusively to home town customers, explain why we expect c to have a limiting value.

10. **Another table** The following is a partial table of values for $f = f(x)$.

x	0	5	10	15	20
$f = f(x)$	5.7	4.3	1.1	−3.6	−7.9

What is the value of $f(15)$?

11. **Average rate of change:** Using the table in Exercise 10, what is the average rate of decrease for f between $x = 15$ and $x = 20$?

12. **Using average rate of decrease:** Use the average rate of decrease calculated above to estimate the value of $f(17)$.

Drill exercises for Section 1.3

1. **A function given by a graph** The following is the graph of a function $f = f(x)$.

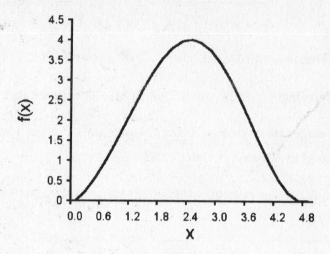

What is the value of $f(1.8)$?

2. **An x value for a given f value** Using the graph from Exercise 1, what is the smallest value of x for which $f(x) = 1.5$?

3. **The maximum:** Where does the graph in Exercise 1 reach a maximum, and what is that maximum value?

4. **Increasing functions:** Where is the graph in Exercise 1 increasing?

5. **Decreasing functions:** Where is the graph in Exercise 1 decreasing?

6. **Concavity:** What is the concavity of the graph in Exercise 1 between $x = 1.8$ and $x = 3$?

7. **Concavity again:** A certain graph is increasing, but at a decreasing rate. Discuss its concavity.

8. **Special points:** What is the mathematical term for points where concavity changes?

9. **Maximum and zero:** Sketch the graph of a function $f = f(x)$ if f has a maximum value of 3 when $x = 2$, and f has a zero at $x = 4$.

10. **Increasing and decreasing:** Sketch a graph which increases from 0 up to 3 and decreases after that.

Drill exercises for Section 1.4

1. **A description:** You have $5000 in a cookie jar. Each month, you spend half of the balance. How much do you have after 4 months?

2. **Light:** It is 93,000,000 miles from the Earth to the Sun. Light travels 186,000 miles per second. How long does it take light to travel from the Sun to the Earth?

3. **A description:** The initial value of a function $f = f(x)$ is 5. (That is, $f(0) = 5$.) Each time x is increased by one, the value of f triples. What is the value of $f(4)$? Verify that the formula $f(x) = 5 \times 3^x$ gives that same answer.

4. **Getting a formula:** You sell lemonade for 25 cents per glass. You invested $2.00 in the ingredients. Write a formula that gives the profit $P = P(n)$ as a function of the number n of glasses you sell.

5. **Getting a formula:** Each time a certain balding gentleman showers, he loses 67 strands of hair down the shower drain. Write a formula that gives the total number $N = N(s)$ of hairs lost by the poor man after s showers.

6. **Getting a formula:** You pay $500 to rent a special area in a restaurant. In addition, you pay $10 for each guest. Write a formula that gives your total cost C in dollars as as function of the number n of dinner guests.

7. **Getting a formula:** You currently have $500 in the bank. You add $37 to the account each month. Find a formula that gives your balance B in dollars after t months.

8. **Getting a formula:** An object is removed from a hot oven and left to cool. After t minutes, the difference in the temperature of the object and room temperature, 75 degrees, is 325×0.07^t. Find a formula for the temperature T of the object t minutes after it is removed from the oven.

9. **Proportionality:** For a certain function $f = f(x)$, f is proportional to x, and the constant of proportionality is 8. Find a formula for f.

10. **Constant of proportionality:** If $g(t) = 16t$, then g is proportional to t. What is the constant of proportionality?

Drill exercises for Section 2.1

1. **Making a table:** Make a table for $f(x) = x^2 - 1$ showing function values for $x = 4, 6, 8, \ldots$

2. **Comparing functions:** Make a table which shows a comparison of the values of f from Exercise 1 with those of $g = 2^x$. (Use the same TABLE SETUP values as in Exercise 1.)

3. **Making a table:** Make a table for $f(x) = 16 - x^3$ showing function values for $x = 3, 7, 11, \ldots$

4. **Comparing functions:** Make a table which shows a comparison of the values of f from Exercise 3 with those of $g = 23 - 2^x$. (Use the same TABLE SETUP values as in Exercise 3.)

5. **Finding a limiting value:** It is a fact that the function $\dfrac{4x^2 - 1}{7x^2 + 1}$ has a limiting value. Use a table of values to estimate the limiting value. (Suggestion: We suggest starting the table at 0 and using a table increment of 20. Also, use $\boxed{\nabla}$ to view the extended table.)

6. **Finding a limiting value:** It is a fact that the function $\dfrac{2 + 3^{-x}}{5 - 3^{-x}}$ has a limiting value. Use a table of values to estimate the limiting value. (Suggestion: We suggest starting the table at 0 and using a table increment of 2. Also, use $\boxed{\nabla}$ to view the extended table.)

7. **Finding a minimum:** Suppose the function $f = x^2 - 8x + 21$ describes a physical situation which only makes sense for whole numbers between 0 and 20 (e.g., family expense as a function of number of children). For what value of x does f reach a minimum, and what is that minimum value? (Suggestion: We suggest a table starting at 0 with a table increment of 1.)

8. **Finding a minimum** Suppose the function $f = \dfrac{x^4}{30} - 9x + 50$ describes a physical situation which only makes sense for whole numbers between 0 and 10 (e.g., family expense as a function of number of children). For what value of x does f reach a minimum, and what is the minimum value? (Suggestion: We suggest beginning with a table starting at 0 with a table increment of 1 and then panning further down the table.)

9. **Finding a maximum** Suppose the function $f = 9x^2 - 2^x + 1$ describes a physical situation which only makes sense for whole numbers between 0 and 10 (e.g., family expense as a function of number of children). For what value of x does f reach a maximum, and what is the maximum value? (Suggestion: We suggest beginning with a table starting at 0 with a table increment of 1 and then panning further down the table.)

10. **Finding a maximum:** Suppose the function $f = 3 \times 2^x - 2.15^x$ describes a physical situation which only makes sense for whole numbers between 0 and 15 (e.g., family expense as a function of number of children). For what value of x does f reach a maximum, and what is that maximum value? (<u>Suggestion</u>: We suggest a table starting at 0 with a table increment of 1.)

Drill exercises for Section 2.2

1. **Graphs and function values:** Get the ZStandard view of the graph of $f = 2 - x^2$. Use the graph to get the value of $f(3)$.

2. **Graphs and function values:** Get the ZStandard view of the graph of $f = \dfrac{x^3}{30} + 1$. Use the graph to get the value of $f(3)$.

3. **Graphs and function values:** Get the ZStandard view of the graph of $f = \dfrac{x^2 + 2^x}{x + 10}$. Use the graph to get the value of $f(3)$.

4. **Zooming in:** Get the ZStandard view of $x - \dfrac{x^4}{75}$. Then zoom in once near the peak of the graph.

5. **Finding a window:** Find an appropriate window setup which will show a good graph of $\dfrac{x^3}{500}$ with a horizontal span of -3 to 3.

6. **Finding a window:** Find an appropriate window setup which will show a good graph of $2^x - x^2$ with a horizontal span of 0 to 5.

7. **Finding a window:** Find an appropriate window setup which will show a good graph of $\dfrac{x^4 + 1}{x^2 + 1}$ with a horizontal span of 0 to 300.

8. **Finding a window:** Find an appropriate window setup which will show a good graph of $\sqrt{x^2 + 10} - \sqrt{x^2 + 5}$ with a horizontal span of 0 to 10.

9. **Finding a window:** Find an appropriate window setup which will show a good graph of $\dfrac{1}{x^2 + 1}$ with a horizontal span of -2 to 2.

10. **Two graphs** Show the graphs of $f = x + 1$ and $g = 3 - x$ together on the same screen. (Use the ZStandard viewing window.)

Drill exercises for Section 2.3

1. **Linear equations:** Solve $3x + 7 = x + 21$ for x.

2. **Linear equations:** Solve $2x + 4 = 5x - 12$ for x.

3. **Linear equations:** Solve $3 - 5x = 23 + 4x$ for x.

4. **Linear equations:** Solve $13x + 4 = 5x + 33$ for x.

5. **Linear equations:** Solve $12x + 4 = 55x + 42$ for x.

6. **Linear equations:** Solve $6 - x = 16 + x$ for x.

7. **Linear equations:** Solve for x: $cx + d = 12$.

8. **Linear equations:** Solve for p: $cp = r$.

9. **Linear equations:** Solve for k: $2k + m = 5k + n$.

10. **Linear equations:** Solve for t: $tx^2 = t + 1$.

Drill exercises for Section 2.4

1. **The crossing graphs method:** Solve using the crossing graphs method: $\dfrac{20}{1 + 2^x} = x$

2. **The crossing graphs method:** Solve using the crossing graphs method: $x^2 - x^3 + 3 = \dfrac{x^5}{20}$.

3. **The crossing graphs method:** Solve using the crossing graphs method: $3^x + x = 2^x + 1$.

4. **The crossing graphs method:** Solve using the crossing graphs method: $\sqrt{x^2 + 1} = x^3 + \sqrt{x^4 + 2}$.

5. **Crossing graphs:** Solve $\dfrac{5}{x^2 + x + 1} = 1$ using the crossing graphs method. (<u>Note</u>: There are two solutions. Find them both.)

6. **The single graph method:** Use the single graph method to solve $\dfrac{20}{1 + 2^x} = x$.

7. **The single graph method:** Use the single graph method to solve $\dfrac{5}{x^2 + x + 1} = 1$ (<u>Note</u>: There are two solutions. Find them both.)

8. **The single graph method:** Use the single graph method to solve $3^x = 8$.

9. **The single graph method:** Use the single graph method to solve $\dfrac{-x^4}{x^2+1} = -1$. (Note: There are two solutions. Find them both.

10. **The single graph method:** Use the single graph method to solve $x^3 = x + 5$.

Drill exercises for Section 2.5

1. **Maximum:** Find the maximum value of $5x + 4 - x^2$ on the horizontal span of 0 to 5.

2. **Minimum:** Find the minimum value of $2^x - x^2 + 5$ on the horizontal span of 0 to 5.

3. **Minimum:** Find the minimum value of $x + \dfrac{x+5}{x^2+1}$ on the horizontal span of 0 to 5.

4. **Maximum:** Find the maximum value of $5x^2 - e^x$ on the horizontal span of 0 to 5.

5. **Maximum:** Find the maximum value of $x^{1/x}$ on the horizontal span of 0 to 10.

6. **Maximum:** Find the minimum value of $4e^{2x} + 3x^2$ on the horizontal span of -2 to 1.

7. **Maxima and minima:** Find all maxima and minima of $f = x^3 - 6x + 1$ with a horizontal span from -2 to 2 and a vertical span from -10 to 10.

8. **Maxima and minima:** Find all maxima and minima of $f = \dfrac{8x}{1+x^2}$. Use a horizontal span of -5 to 5.

9. **End point maximum:** Find the maximum value of $x^3 + x$ on the horizontal span of 0 to 5.

10. **End point minimum:** Find the minimum value of $200 - x^3$ on the horizontal span of 0 to 5.

Drill exercises for Section 3.1

1. **Slope from rise and run:** One end of a ladder is on the ground. The top of the ladder rests at the top of an 8-foot wall. The wall is 2 horizontal feet from the base of the ladder. What is the slope of the line made by the ladder? (Assume the positive direction points from the base of the ladder toward the wall.)

2. **Slope from rise and run:** One end of a ladder is on the ground. The top of the ladder rests at the top of an 15-foot wall. The wall is 3 horizontal feet from the base of the ladder. What is the slope of the line made by the ladder? (Assume the positive direction points from the base of the ladder toward the wall.)

3. **Height from slope and horizontal distance:** The base of a ladder is 3 horizontal feet from a wall where its top rests. The slope of the line made by the ladder is 2.5. What is the vertical height of the top of the ladder? (Assume the positive direction points from the base of the ladder toward the wall.)

4. **Height from slope and horizontal distance:** The base of a ladder is 4 horizontal feet from a wall where its top rests. The slope of the line made by the ladder is 1.7. What is the vertical height of the top of the ladder? (Assume the positive direction points from the base of the ladder toward the wall.)

5. **Horizontal distance from height and slope:** A ladder leans against a wall so that its slope is 1.75. The top of the ladder is 9 vertical feet above the ground. What is the horizontal distance from the base of the ladder to the wall? (Assume the positive direction points from the base of the ladder toward the wall.)

6. **Horizontal distance from height and slope:** A ladder leans against a wall so that its slope is 2.1. The top of the ladder is 12 vertical feet above the ground. What is the horizontal distance from the base of the ladder to the wall? (Assume the positive direction points from the base of the ladder toward the wall.)

7. **Slope from two points:** Take west to be the positive direction. The height of a sloped roof above the place I stand is 12 feet. If I move 3 feet west, the height is 10 feet. What is the slope?

8. **Continuation of Exercise 7:** If I move 5 additional feet west, what is the height of the roof?

9. **A circus tent:** I am at the center of a circus tent, where the height is 22 feet. I am facing due west, which I take to be the positive direction. The slope of the tent line is -0.8. If I walk 7 feet west, how high is the tent?

10. **More on the circus tent:** Assume the roof of the circus tent in Exercise 9 extends in a straight line to the ground. How far from the center of the tent does the roof meet the ground?

Drill exercises for Section 3.2

1. **Slope from two values:** Suppose f is a linear function so that $f(2) = 7$ and $f(5) = 19$. What is the slope of f?

2. **Slope from two values:** Suppose f is a linear function so that $f(3) = 9$ and $f(8) = 5$. What is the slope of f?

3. **Function value from slope and run:** Suppose f is a linear function so that $f(3) = 7$. If the slope of f is 2.7, then what is $f(5)$?

4. **Function value from slope and run:** Suppose f is a linear function so that $f(5) = 2$. If the slope of f is 3.1, then what is $f(12)$?

5. **Run from slope and rise:** Suppose that f is a linear function with slope -3.4 and that $f(1) = 6$. What value of x gives $f(x) = 0$?

6. **Run from slope and rise:** Suppose that f is a linear function with slope 2.6 and that $f(5) = -3$. What value of x gives $f(x) = 0$?

7. **Linear equation from slope and point:** Suppose that f is a linear function with slope 4 and that $f(3) = 5$. Find the equation for f.

8. **Linear equation from slope and point:** Suppose that f is a linear function with slope -3 and that $f(2) = 8$. Find the equation for f.

9. **Linear equation from two points:** Suppose f is a linear function so that $f(4) = 8$ and $f(9) = 2$. Find the equation for f.

10. **Linear equation from two points:** Suppose f is a linear function so that $f(3) = 5$ and $f(7) = -4$. Find the equation for f.

Drill exercises for Section 3.3

1. **Testing data for linearity:** Test the following data set to see if the data is linear.

x	2	4	6	8
y	12	17	22	27

2. **Testing data for linearity:** Test the following data set to see if the data is linear.

x	2	4	6	8
y	12	17	21	25

3. **Making a linear model:** Make a linear model for the data in Exercise 1.

4. **Making a linear model:** The data in Exercise 2 is not linear, but, if we omit the first point, the remaining data is liner. Make a linear model for these last three points.

5. **Graphing discrete data:** Plot the data from the table in Exercise 2 above.

6. **Adding a graph to a data plot:** Add the graph of $y = 2.5x + 7$ to the data plot from Exercise 5.

7. **Entering and graphing data:** Enter the following data and plot f against x.

x	1	2	3	4	5
f	8	6	5	3	1

8. **Adding a graph:** Add to the picture in Exercise 7 the graph of $-1.7x + 9.7$.

9. **Editing data:** Plot the squares of the data points in the table from Exercise 1.

10. **Data that is linear:** Plot the data from Exercise 1 along with the linear model from Exercise 3.

Drill exercises for Section 3.4

1. **Slope of regression line:** The slope of the regression line for a certain data set is a positive number. Do you expect the data values to be increasing or decreasing?

2. **Meaning of slope of regression line:** For a certain school district, the slope of the regression line for money spent on education as a function of the year is $2300 per year. What does this mean in practical terms?

3. **Meaning of slope of regression line:** The slope of the regression line for federal agricultural spending is larger than the slope of the regression line for federal spending on research and development. Explain in practical terms what this relationship means.

4. **Meaning of slope of regression line:** For many animals, speed running (in miles per hour) is approximately a linear function of the length (in inches) of the animal. The slope of the regression line for speed running as a function of length is 1.38. Explain in practical terms what this means.

5. **Plotting data and regression lines:** For the following data set: (a) Plot the data. (b) Find the equation of the regression line. (c) Add the graph of the regression line to the plot of the data points.

x	1	2	3	4	5
y	2.3	2	1.8	1.4	1.3

6. **Plotting data and regression lines:** For the following data set: (a) Plot the data. (b) Find the equation of the regression line. (c) Add the graph of the regression line to the plot of the data points.

x	1.3	2.5	3.3	4.2	5.1
y	2.6	2.6	2	1.8	1.5

7. **Plotting data and regression lines:** For the following data set: (a) Plot the data. (b) Find the equation of the regression line. (c) Add the graph of the regression line to the plot of the data points.

x	2.3	3.7	5.1	6.4	8.2
y	4.8	5.3	7.2	9.6	10.3

8. **Plotting data and regression lines:** For the following data set: (a) Plot the data. (b) Find the equation of the regression line. (c) Add the graph of the regression line to the plot of the data points.

x	4.1	5.7	7.3	8.9	10.5
y	7.7	8.3	8.4	8.9	9.1

9. **Plotting data and regression lines:** For the following data set: (a) Plot the data. (b) Find the equation of the regression line. (c) Add the graph of the regression line to the plot of the data points.

x	5.2	8.9	12.6	16.3	20
y	−3.1	−4.8	−5.3	−7.1	−7.9

10. **Plotting data and regression lines:** For the following data set: (a) Plot the data. (b) Find the equation of the regression line. (c) Add the graph of the regression line to the plot of the data points.

x	16.3	20	23.7	27.4	31.1
y	51.1	68.8	80.3	86.2	99.6

Drill exercises for Section 3.5

1. **An explanation:** Explain why the solution of a system of two equations in two unknowns is the intersection point of the two graphs.

2. **What is the solution?** For a certain system of two linear equations in two unknowns, the graphs are distinct parallel lines. What can you conclude about the solution of the system of equations?

3. **Crossing graphs:** Solve using crossing graphs.

$$3x + 4y = 6$$
$$2x - 6y = 5$$

4. **Crossing graphs:** Solve using crossing graphs.

$$-7x + 21y = 79$$
$$13x + 17y = 6$$

5. **Crossing graphs:** Solve using crossing graphs.

$$0.7x + 5.3y = 6.6$$
$$5.2x + 2.2y = 1.7$$

6. **Crossing graphs:** Solve using crossing graphs.

$$-6.6x - 26.5y = 17.1$$
$$6.9x + 5.5y = 8.4$$

7. **Hand calculation:** Solve the system of equations in Exercise 3 by hand calculation.

8. **Hand calculation:** Solve the system of equations in Exercise 4 by hand calculation.

9. **Hand calculation:** Solve the system of equations in Exercise 5 by hand calculation.

10. **Hand calculation:** Solve the system of equations in Exercise 6 by hand calculation.

Drill exercises for Section 4.1

1. **Function value from initial value and growth factor:** Suppose that f is an exponential function with growth factor 2.4 and that $f(0) = 3$. Find $f(2)$. Find a formula for $f(x)$.

2. **Function value from initial value and decay factor:** Suppose that f is an exponential function with decay factor 0.094 and that $f(0) = 400$. Find $f(2)$. Find a formula for $f(x)$.

3. **Finding the growth factor:** Suppose that f is an exponential function with $f(4) = 8$ and $f(5) = 10$. What is the growth factor for f?

4. **Exponential decay:** Is the graph of exponential decay versus time increasing or decreasing?

5. **Rate of change:** What can be said about the rate of change of an exponential function?

6. **Percentage growth:** A certain phenomenon has an initial value of 10 and grows at a rate of 7% per year. Give an exponential function which describes this phenomenon.

7. **Percentage decay:** A certain phenomenon has initial value 10 and decays by 4% each year. Give an exponential function which describes this phenomenon.

8. **Changing units:** A certain phenomenon has a yearly growth factor of 1.17. What is its monthly growth factor? What is its decade growth factor?

9. **Percentage change:** A bank account grows by 9% each year. By what percentage does it grow each month?

10. **Percentage change:** A certain radioactive substance decays at a rate of 17% each year. By what percentage does it decay each month?

Drill exercises for Section 4.2

1. **Finding the growth factor:** $N = N(t)$ is an exponential function with initial value 7. If t is increased by one, N is multiplied by 8. Find a formula for N.

2. **Finding the growth factor:** $N = N(t)$ is an exponential function with initial value 6. If t is increased by one, N is divided by 13. Find a formula for N.

3. **Finding the growth factor:** $N = N(t)$ is an exponential function with initial value 12. If t is increased by 7, the effect is to multiply N by 62. Find a formula for N

4. **Finding initial value:** $N = N(t)$ is an exponential function with growth factor 1.94, and $N(5) = 6$. Find a formula for N.

5. **Exponential function from two points:** $N = N(t)$ is an exponential function so that $N(4) = 9$ and $N(7) = 22$. Find a formula for N.

6. **Testing exponential data:** Determine if the following table shows exponential data.

x	0	1	2	3
y	2.6	7.8	23.4	70.2

7. **Testing exponential data:** Determine if the following table shows exponential data.

x	0	2	4	6
y	5	10	20	40

8. **Testing exponential data:** Determine if the following table shows exponential data.

x	0	2	4	6
y	5	9	21	43

9. **Modeling exponential data:** Make an exponential model for the data from Exercise 7.

10. **Modeling exponential data:** Make an exponential model for the data from Exercise 6.

Drill exercises for Section 4.3

1. **Exponential transformation:** If the table of values

input value	a	b	...
function value	z	w	...

is linear data, then what kind of data would appear in the following table?

input value	a	b	...
function value	e^z	e^w	...

2. **Logarithmic conversion:** If the table of values

input value	a	b	...
function value	z	w	...

is exponential data, then what kind of data would appear in the following table?

input value	a	b	...
function value	$\ln z$	$\ln w$	...

3. **Slope and growth factor:** The slope of the regression line for exponential data is -0.77. Find the decay factor for the exponential function.

4. **Regression line to exponential model:** The regression line for the logarithm of exponential data is $y = 3x + 4$. Find the exponential model for the data.

5. **Exponential regression:** Use exponential regression to fit the following data set. Give the exponential model, and plot the data along with the model.

x	1	2	3	4	5
y	4.1	8.7	19.2	28.6	64.7

6. **Exponential regression:** Use exponential regression to fit the following data set. Give the exponential model, and plot the data along with the model.

x	1	2	3	4	5
y	0.7	0.3	0.1	0.05	0.01

7. **Exponential regression:** Use exponential regression to fit the following data set. Give the exponential model, and plot the data along with the model.

x	4.2	7.9	10.8	15.5	20.2
y	7.5	8.1	8.5	10.2	12.3

8. **Exponential regression:** Use exponential regression to fit the following data set. Give the exponential model, and plot the data along with the model.

x	22.4	27.3	29.4	34.1	38.6
y	0.053	0.025	0.011	0.005	0.002

9. **Exponential regression:** Use exponential regression to fit the following data set. Give the exponential model, and plot the data along with the model.

x	1	2	3	4	5
y	3.7	4.3	6.1	9.1	13.6

10. **Exponential regression:** Use exponential regression to fit the following data set. Give the exponential model, and plot the data along with the model.

x	3	7	9	10	15
y	33.5	988.8	5470.8	12,830	893,442

Drill exercises for Section 4.4

1. **APR, yearly compounding:** A loan is made at 10% APR. If interest were compounded yearly, what would be the yearly growth factor for the loan?

2. **APR, continuous compounding:** A loan is made at 10% APR. If interest is compounded continuously, what is the yearly growth factor for the loan? What is the EAR?

3. **Growth factor:** What is the growth factor for the exponential function $7.6e^{4.3t}$?

4. **Changing form for an exponential function:** The exponential function 3×0.77^t can be written in the alternative form Pe^{rt}. Write it in this way.

5. **Changing form for an exponential function:** The exponential function 5×5.34^t can be written in the alternative form Pe^{rt}. Write it in this way.

6. **Changing form for an exponential function:** The exponential function 4×9.6^t can be written in the alternative form Pe^{rt}. Write it in this way.

7. **Changing form for an exponential function:** The exponential function $7e^{6.8t}$ can be written in the form Pa^t. Write it in this way.

8. **Changing form for an exponential function:** The exponential function $3e^{-2.5t}$ can be written in the form Pa^t. Write it in this way.

9. **Unit conversion:** A certain quantity grows according to the formula $12e^{24t}$, where t is measured in years. How would you write this formula if time is measured in months?

10. **Unit conversion:** A certain quantity grows according to the formula $12e^{3.67t}$, where t is measured in years. How would you write this formula if time is measured in decades?

Drill exercises for Section 5.1

1. **Graph of a power function:** If k is negative, then is the graph of x^k increasing or decreasing for $x > 0$?

2. **Graph of a power function:** If k is positive, then is the graph of x^k increasing or decreasing for $x > 0$?

3. **Homogeneity:** $f(x) = cx^{1.47}$. If x is tripled, by what factor is f increased?

4. **Homogeneity:** $f(x) = cx^{2.53}$. By what factor must x be increased in order to triple the value of f?

5. **Homogeneity:** $f(x) = cx^{3.11}$. How do the function values $f(3.6)$ and $f(5.5)$ compare?

6. **Homogeneity:** $f(x) = cx^{3.11}$. $f(y)$ is 9 times as large as $f(z)$. How do y and z compare?

7. **Homogeneity:** $f(x) = cx^k$. $f(6.6)$ is 6.2 times as large as $f(1.76)$. What is the value of k?

8. **Constant term:** $f(x) = cx^{4.2}$ and $f(4) = 8$. Find the value of c.

9. **Constant term:** $f(x) = cx^{-1.32}$ and $f(5) = 11$. Find the value of c.

10. **Exponential versus power functions:** Which function is eventually the largest: x^{1023} or 1.0002^x?

Drill exercises for Section 5.2

1. **Logarithmic conversion of both x and y:** If the table of values

input value	a	b	...
function value	z	w	...

   is power data, then what kind of data would appear in the following table?

input value	$\ln a$	$\ln b$	...
function value	$\ln z$	$\ln w$	...

2. **Formula conversion:** Suppose $\ln f = 3 \ln x + 2$. What kind of function is $f = f(x)$? Find a formula for f.

3. **Getting the power:** If the regression line for $\ln y$ as a linear function of $\ln x$ has slope 3, what is the power used to express y as a power function of x?

4. **Getting c:** If the regression line for $\ln y$ as a linear function of $\ln x$ has initial value 4, what is the value of c in the formula $y = cx^k$?

5. **Modeling power data:** The following data table was generated by a power function f. Find a formula for f and plot the data points along with the graph of the formula.

x	1	2	3	4	5
f	3.6	8.86	15.02	21.83	29.17

6. **Modeling almost power data:** Model the following data with a power function. Give the formula and plot the data points along with the model.

x	1	2	3	4	5
f	6.3	1.9	0.6	0.2	0.07

7. **Modeling almost power data:** Model the following data with a power function. Give the formula and plot the data points along with the model.

x	1	2	3	4	5
f	2.2	51.7	338.9	1236.4	3177.8

8. **Modeling almost power data:** Model the following data with a power function. Give the formula and plot the data points along with the model.

x	1	2	3	4	5
f	5.5	15.1	28.8	63.1	84.2

9. **Modeling almost power data:** Model the following data with a power function. Give the formula and plot the data points along with the model.

x	0.3	1.3	2.2	3.3	4.1
f	5.6	2	0.92	0.77	0.51

10. **The common logarithm:** Repeat Exercise 6 using the common logarithm.

Drill exercises for Section 5.3

1. **Period and amplitude:** Find a formula for a function with period 17 and amplitude 4. Graph it over two periods.

2. **Period and amplitude:** Find a formula for a function with period 6 and amplitude 3. Graph it over two periods.

3. **Right triangle trigonometry:** For an acute angle θ of a certain right triangle, the adjacent side has length 5, the opposite side has length 12, and the hypotenuse has length 13. Find $\sin\theta$, $\cos\theta$, and $\tan\theta$.

4. **Calculating height:** A man sits 331 horizontal feet from the base of a wall. He must incline his eyes at an angle of 16.2 degrees to look at the top of the wall. How tall is the wall?

5. **Calculating height:** A man sits 222 horizontal feet from the base of a wall. He must incline his eyes at an angle of 6.4 degrees to look at the top of the wall. How tall is the wall?

6. **Calculating an angle:** A man sits 270 horizontal feet from the base of a wall which is 76 feet high. At what angle must he incline his eyes in order to look at the top of the wall?

7. **Calculating an angle:** A wall is 38 feet high. A man sits on the ground and finds the distance from himself to the top of the wall is 83 feet. At what angle must he incline his eyes in order to look at the top of the wall?

8. **Calculating distance:** This is a continuation of Exercise 7: What is the horizontal distance of the man from the wall?

9. **Calculating distance:** A man sits 130 horizontal feet from the base of a wall. He must incline his eyes at an angle of 13 degrees to look at the top of the wall. What is the distance from the man directly to the top of the wall?

10. **Calculating distance:** A man sits 18 horizontal feet from the base of a wall. He must incline his eyes at an angle of 21 degrees to look at the top of the wall. What is the distance from the man directly to the top of the wall?

11. **Determining period and amplitude:** What is the period and amplitude of $18\sin(3.98\theta)$?

Drill exercises for Section 5.4

1. **The rate of change:** What can be said about the rate of change of a quadratic function?

2. **Testing for quadratic data:** Test the following data table to see if it is quadratic.

x	1	2	3	4	5
y	0	3	10	21	36

3. **Testing for quadratic data:** Test the following data table to see if it is quadratic.

x	1	2	3	4	5
y	1	5	9	24	37

4. **Quadratic formula:** Use the quadratic formula to solve $3x^2 - 5x + 1 = 0$.

5. **Quadratic formula:** Use the quadratic formula to solve $-2x^2 + 2x + 5 = 0$.

6. **Quadratic formula:** Use the quadratic formula to solve $5x^2 - 8 = 0$.

7. **Recognizing polynomials:** Which of the following functions are polynomials? Give the degree of each function that is a polynomial.

   (a) $x^8 - 17x + 1$

   (b) $\sqrt{x} + 8$

   (c) $9.7x - 53.1x^4$

   (d) $x^{3.2} - x^{2.3}$

8. **Testing for polynomial data:** Explain how one tests data to see if it represents a polynomial of degree n.

9. **Rational functions:** What is a rational function?

10. **Single graph method:** Use the single graph method to solve the quadratic equation in Exercise 4.

Drill exercises for Section 6.1

1. **Velocity:** What is the rate of change in directed distance?

2. **Sign of velocity:** When directed distance is decreasing, is velocity positive or negative? What is the velocity when directed distance is not changing?

3. **Sign of velocity:** When the graph of directed distance is decreasing, is the graph of velocity above or below the horizontal axis?

4. **Constant velocity:** When velocity is constant, what kind of function is directed distance?

5. **Constant velocity:** When the graph of directed distance is a straight line, what can be said about the graph of velocity?

6. **At a valley:** When the graph of directed distance reaches a minimum (at a valley), what is the velocity?

7. **A car:** A car is driving at a constant velocity of 60 miles per hour. A perspective has been chosen so that directed distance is increasing. Since velocity is constant, we know that directed distance is a linear function. What is the slope of that linear function?

8. **A trip:** A car is driving on a highway that leads west from home. We locate its position as distance west from home. In each of the following situations determine if velocity is positive, negative, or zero.

    (a) The car is driving west.

    (b) The car is stopped at a traffic light.

    (c) The car is driving east.

9. **A rock:** A rock is tossed upward and reaches its peak 2 seconds after the toss. Its location is determined by its distance up from the ground. What is the sign of velocity at each of the following times?

   (a) 1 second after the toss.

   (b) 2 seconds after the toss.

   (c) 3 seconds after the toss.

10. **Graph of velocity:** If the graph of velocity lies on the horizontal axis, what can be said about the graph of directed distance?

Drill exercises for Section 6.2

1. **Meaning of rate of change:** What is the common term for the rate of change of each of the following phenomena?

   (a) Directed distance as a function of time.

   (b) Velocity as a function of time.

   (c) Tax due as a function of income.

   (d) Profit as a function of dollars invested.

2. **A mathematical term** If $f = f(x)$, then we use $\dfrac{df}{dx}$ to denote the rate of change in f. What is the technical mathematical term for $\dfrac{df}{dx}$?

3. **Sign of the derivative:** Suppose $f = f(x)$. What is the sign of $\dfrac{df}{dx}$ in each of the following situations?

   (a) The function f is increasing.

   (b) The graph of f has reached a peak.

   (c) The function f is decreasing.

   (d) The graph of f is a horizontal line.

4. **Constant rate of change:** When $\dfrac{df}{dx}$ is constant, what kind of function is f?

5. **A value for the rate of change:** If $\dfrac{df}{dx}$ has a constant value of 10, we know that f is a linear function. What is the slope of f?

6. **Elevation:** If $E(t)$ is your elevation at time t, and you are walking up a steep slope, what can be said about $\dfrac{dE}{dt}$?

7. **Marginal tax rate:** You have the opportunity to earn some extra income working at $20 per hour. If your marginal tax rate is 34%, how much of the hourly wage will you get to keep?

8. **Graph of rate of change:** What can be said about the graph of $\dfrac{df}{dx}$ in the following situations?

   (a) The graph of f is increasing.

   (b) The graph of f is at a peak.

   (c) The graph of f is decreasing.

   (d) The graph of f is a straight line.

9. **Graph of f:** What can be said about the graph of f if the graph of $\dfrac{df}{dx}$ is below the horizontal axis?

10. **Advertising:** Let $s(a)$ denote sales generated by spending a dollars on advertising. My goal is to increase sales. If $\dfrac{ds}{da}$ is negative, should I spend more or less money on advertising?

Drill exercises for Section 6.3

1. **Technical terms:** What is the common mathematical term for an equation of change?

2. **Linear function:** If f satisfies the equation of change $\dfrac{df}{dx} = m$, what kind of function is f?

3. **Slope:** If f satisfies the equation of change $\dfrac{df}{dx} = 5$, then f is a linear function. What is the slope of f?

4. **Exponential functions:** If f satisfies the equation of change $\dfrac{df}{dx} = cf$, what kind of function is f?

5. **Solving an equation of change:** If f satisfies the equation of change $\dfrac{df}{dx} = 8f$, then f is an exponential function and hence can be written as $f = Ae^{ct}$. Find the value of c.

6. **Why equations of change:** List some commonly occurring phenomena which satisfy the equation of change $\dfrac{df}{dx} = cf$.

7. **A leaky balloon:** A balloon leaks air (changes volume) at a rate one third the volume per minute. Write an equation of change which describes the volume V of air in the balloon at time t in minutes.

8. **Solving an equation of change:** Solve the equation of change from Exercise 7 if there is initially 4 liters of air in the balloon.

9. **Solving an equation of change:** Solve the equation of change $\frac{df}{dx} = 3$ if the initial value of f is 7.

10. **A falling rock:** Let t be time in seconds and $v = v(t)$ the velocity (in feet per second) of a falling rock. The acceleration of the rock has a constant value of 32 feet per second per second. Write an equation of change satisfied by v.

Drill exercises for Section 6.4

1. **Equilibrium solutions:** What is an equilibrium solution of an equation of change?

2. **More equilibrium solutions:** If $f = 10$ is an equilibrium solution of an equation of change involving $\frac{df}{dx}$, what is the value of $\frac{df}{dx}$ when f is 10?

3. **Finding equilibrium solutions:** Find an equilibrium solution of $\frac{df}{dx} = 2f - 6$.

4. **Sketching graphs:** Consider the equation of change $\frac{df}{dx} = 2f - 6$.

   (a) What is the sign of $\frac{df}{dx}$ when f is less than 3?

   (b) What can you say about the graph of f versus x when f is less than 3?

   (c) What is the sign of $\frac{df}{dx}$ when f is greater than 3?

   (d) What can you say about the graph of f versus x when f is greater than 3?

5. **Water:** Water flows into a tank and a certain part of it drains out through a valve. The volume v in cubic feet of water in the tank at time t satisfies the equation $\frac{dv}{dt} = 5 - \frac{v}{3}$. If the process continues for a long time, how much water will be in the tank?

6. **Water:** At some time in the process described in Exercise 5 there are 23 cubic feet of water in the tank. Is the volume of water increasing or decreasing?

7. **Water:** At some time in the process described in Exercise 5 there are 8 cubic feet of water in the tank. Is the volume increasing or decreasing?

8. **Population:** A certain population grows according to $\frac{dN}{dt} = 0.03N\left(1 - \frac{N}{6300}\right)$. What is the carrying capacity of the environment for this particular population?

9. **Population:** At some time, the population described in Exercise 8 is at the level $N = 4238$. Is the population level increasing or decreasing?

10. **Population:** At some time, the population described in Exercise 8 is at the level $N = 8716$. Is the population level increasing or decreasing?

Drill exercises for Section 6.5

1. **Rate of change for a linear function:** If f is the linear function $f = 7x - 3$, what is the value of $\frac{df}{dx}$?

2. **Rate of change from data:** Suppose $f = f(x)$ satisfies $f(2) = 5$ and $f(2.005) = 5.012$. Estimate the value of $\frac{df}{dx}$ at $x = 2$.

3. **Rate of change from data:** Suppose $f = f(x)$ satisfies $f(3) = 8$ and $f(3.005) = 7.972$. Estimate the value of $\frac{df}{dx}$ at $x = 3$.

4. **Estimating rates of change:** By direct calculation, estimate the value of $\frac{df}{dx}$ for $f(x) = x^2 + 1$ at $x = 3$. Use an increment of 0.0001.

5. **Estimating rates of change:** By direct calculation, estimate the value of $\frac{df}{dx}$ for $f(x) = \frac{1}{x^2}$ at $x = 4$. Use an increment of 0.0001.

6. **Estimating rates of change with the calculator:** Make a graph of $x^3 - x^2$ and use the calculator to estimate its rate of change at $x = 3$. (We recommend a $\boxed{\text{WINDOW}}$ setting of Xmin=0 , Xmax=4 , Ymin=0 , and Ymax=30 .)

7. **Estimating rates of change with the calculator:** Make a graph of $x + \frac{1}{x}$ and use the calculator to estimate its rate of change at $x = 3$. (We recommend a $\boxed{\text{WINDOW}}$ setting of Xmin=1 , Xmax=4 , Ymin=0 , and Ymax=5 .)

8. **Estimating rates of change with the calculator:** Make a graph of 2^x and use the calculator to estimate its rate of change at $x = 3$. (We recommend a $\boxed{\text{WINDOW}}$ setting of Xmin=0 , Xmax=4 , Ymin=0 , and Ymax=20 .)

9. **Estimating rates of change with the calculator:** Make a graph of 3^{-x} and use the calculator to estimate its rate of change at $x = 3$. (We recommend a $\boxed{\text{WINDOW}}$ setting of Xmin=0 , Xmax=4 , Ymin= $\boxed{(-)}$ 1 , and Ymax=1 .)

10. **Limiting value of a rate of change:** Looking at the graph of 3^{-x} from Exercise 9, what is $\dfrac{df}{dx}$ for large values of x?

Drill exercises for Section 7.1

1. **Population growth:** If B is births per unit time and D is deaths per unit time, write an equation of change for population N as a function of time t.

2. **An exponential model:** *This is a continuation of Exercise 1 above.* If both B and D are proportional to N, explain how the equation of change above leads to an exponential model.

3. **An exponential model:** *This is a continuation of Exercise 1 above.* Suppose $B = 0.04N$ and $D = 0.013N$. Find the equation of change for exponential growth.

4. **Initial value:** If a population is governed by $\dfrac{dN}{dt} = rN$, then the exponential model for N is $N = N_0 e^{rt}$. What is the physical significance of N_0?

5. **r-value:** If a population is governed by $\dfrac{dN}{dt} = rN$, then the exponential model for N is $N = N_0 e^{rt}$. The constant r depends on the species and the environment, and it is known as the r-value of a species in an environment. Explain the physical significance of r.

6. **Comparing r values:** Two populations grow according the model in Exercise 5. The first population has a larger r-value than the second. What can you conclude about the comparative growth rate of the two populations?

7. **Negative r-value:** Suppose a population which follows the model in Exercise 5 has an r-value of -0.03. What happens to the population over time?

8. **Doubling time:** If a population N grows according to $30e^{0.72t}$, where t is measured in years, how long does it take the population to double in size?

9. **Doubling time:** If a population N grows according to $30e^{rt}$, where t is measured in years, and if the population doubles each 13 years, find the value of r.

10. **Discrete growth:** When breeding occurs only during certain seasons, the exponential model is altered slightly to account for this. What is the name of the altered model?

Drill exercises for Section 7.2

1. **Logistic growth:** If the notion of *environmental carrying capacity* is added to the basic assumptions leading to the exponential model, we get a different model. What is the name of this model?

2. **Logistic equation of change:** What is the equation of change governing the logistic model?

3. **More on the logistic equation of change:** Suppose a certain population grows according to $\frac{dN}{dt} = 0.13N \left(1 - \frac{N}{378} \right)$.

    (a) What is the r-value for this species in this environment?

    (b) What is the environmental carrying capacity?

    (c) What are the equilibrium solutions of the equation?

    (d) At what value of N will there be a maximum growth rate?

4. **Per capita growth rate:** In a population which grows logistically, if the per capita growth rate $\frac{1}{N} \frac{dN}{dt}$ is considered as a function of the population N, what kind of function is it?

5. **Formula for logistic growth:** Write the formula for logistic growth corresponding to the equation of change $\frac{dN}{dt} = rN \left(1 - \frac{N}{K} \right)$.

6. **The formula continued:** *This is a continuation of Exercise 5 above.* Show how the constant b in the formula above can be calculated from initial population and carrying capacity.

7. **More logistic formula:** Write the logistic formula that governs a population which grows logistically with r-value 0.015, carrying capacity 2390, and initial population 120.

8. **Harvesting:** What is the name of the model which says that a renewable resource which grows logistically should be harvested at half the carrying capacity?

9. **Harvesting** Suppose a renewable population grows logistically according to

$$\frac{dN}{dt} = 0.02N \left(1 - \frac{N}{778} \right).$$

    According to the maximum sustainable yield model what is the optimum harvesting level?

10. **Harvesting continued** The maximum sustainable yield model says that a renewable resource which grows logistically should be harvested at half the carrying capacity. What graphical significance does this point have?

Drill exercises for Section 7.3

1. **Groups:** In population dynamics, what is meant by the term "cohort"?

2. **Mortality statistics:** In gathering mortality statistics, it is common to use the letters x, l_x, d_x, q_x. Give the meaning of each of these symbols.

3. **Calculation of mortality statistics:** Show how to calculate q_x from l_x and d_x.

4. **More calculation of mortality statistics:** For a certain population $l_5 = 300$ and $l_6 = 275$. Find d_5 and q_5.

5. **Number of survivors:** A certain cohort begins at 1000 individuals, and by age 31 years 60% have died. What is the value of l_{31}?

6. **Mortality:** For the cohort in Exercise 5, suppose 120 individuals who reach age 31 die before age 32. What is the value of d_{31}?

7. **Mortality:** *This is a continuation of Exercises 5 and 6 above.* Using the information from Exercises 5 and 6, calculate q_{31} and l_{32}.

8. **Survivorship curve:** What is a survivorship curve?

9. **Survivorship curve:** Explain in practical terms what a survivorship curve shows.

10. **The end of a survivorship curve:** Explain why all survivorship curves must eventually touch the horizontal axis.

ANSWERS TO DRILL EXERCISES

Note: The answers presented here are intended to provide help when students encounter difficulties. Complete answers will include appropriate arguments and written explanations which do not appear here. Also, many of the exercises are subject to interpretation, and properly supported answers which are different than those presented here may be considered correct.

Answers for the Prologue

1. 2.43

2. 28.71

3. 1.53

4. 3.42

5. 0.12

6. 12.79

7. 1.32

8. 0.07

9. 0.6

10. −2.02

11. −2.17

12. −0.24

13. (a) 0.62

    (b) 1.03

14. (a) 36,200

    (b) 7,190,000

    (c) 0.00313

    (d) 0.000000467

Answers for Section 1.1

1. 0.35

2. 42,943,441.08

3. 3.67

4. −94.17

5. 1.06

6. 2.18

7. 1.16

8. $p(2.5)$

9. $c(2, 3, 5)$

10. It is the top speed in miles per hour of a fish 13 inches long.

Answers for Section 1.2

1. 23.8

2. $\dfrac{44.6 + 23.8}{2} = 34.2$

3. $\dfrac{44.6 - 23.8}{10} = 2.08$ per unit

4. $23.8 + 3 \times 2.08 = 30.04$

5. $\dfrac{51.3 + 44.6}{2} = 47.95$

6. $\dfrac{51.3 - 44.6}{10} = 0.67$ per unit

7. $44.6 + 7 \times 0.67 = 49.29$

8. About 54.

9. We will sell no more cars than the local population.

10. -3.6

11. 0.86 per unit

12. -5.32

Answers for Section 1.3

1. About 3.3

2. About 1

3. At $x = 2.4$ f is about 4.

4. From 0 to 2.4.

5. From 2.4 to 4.8.

6. Concave down

7. It is concave down.

8. Inflection points

9. Answers will vary. Our solution is shown below.

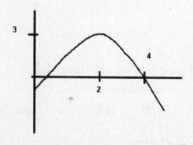

10. Answers will vary, but the graph should have the same shape as the figure in the preceeding exercise except that the maximum should occur at $x = 3$.

Answers for Section 1.4

1. $312.50

2. 500 seconds or about 8.33 minutes

3. 405

4. $P = 0.25n - 2$ dollars

5. $N = 67s$

6. $C = 500 + 10n$

7. $B = 500 + 37t$

8. $T = 75 + 325 \times 0.07^t$

9. $f = 8x$

10. 16

Answers for Section 2.1

1.

X	Y₁	
4	15	
6	35	
8	63	
10	99	
12	143	
14	195	
16	255	
X=4		

2.

X	Y₁	Y₂
4	15	16
6	35	64
8	63	256
10	99	1024
12	143	4096
14	195	16384
16	255	65536
X=4		

3.

X	Y1	
3	-11	
7	-327	
11	-1315	
15	-3359	
19	-6843	
23	-12151	
27	-19667	

X=3

4.

X	Y1	Y2
3	-11	15
7	-327	-105
11	-1315	-2025
15	-3359	-32745
19	-6843	-5.2E5
23	-12151	-8.4E6
27	-19667	-1.3E8

X=3

5.

X	Y1	
0	-1	
20	.57087	
40	.57129	
60	.57137	
80	.57139	
100	.57141	
120	.57141	

X=0

About 0.57143

6.

X	Y1	
0	.75	
2	.43182	
4	.40347	
6	.40038	
8	.40004	
10	.4	
12	.4	

X=0

About 0.4

7.

X	Y1	
0	21	
1	14	
2	9	
3	6	
4	5	
5	6	
6	9	

X=0

f has a minimum value of 5 at $x = 4$.

8.

X	Y1	
0	50	
1	41.033	
2	32.533	
3	25.7	
4	22.533	
5	25.833	
6	39.2	

X=4

f reaches a minimum of 22.53 at $x = 4$.

9.

X	Y1	
4	129	
5	194	
6	261	
7	314	
8	321	
9	210	
10	-123	

X=8

f reaches a maximum of 321 at $x = 8$.

10.

X	Y1	
11	1606.4	
12	2532.2	
13	3601.1	
14	4056	
15	1347.5	
16	-11040	
17	-54965	

X=14

f has a maximum value of 4056.0 at $x =$ 14.

Answers for Section 2.2

1.

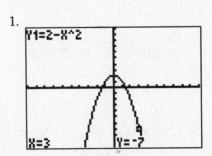

$f(3) = -7$

2.

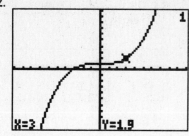

$f(3) = 1.9$

3.

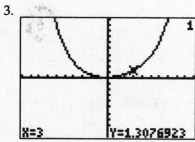

$f(3) = 1.31$

4.

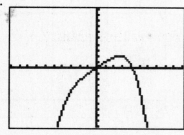

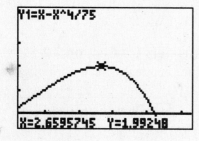

5. From a table we chose a vertical span from -0.06 to 0.06.

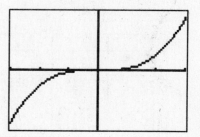

6. From a table we chose a vertical span from -2 to 10.

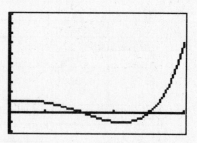

7. From a table we chose a vertical span from 0 to 90,000.

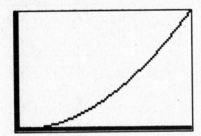

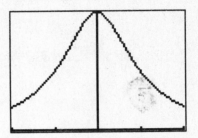

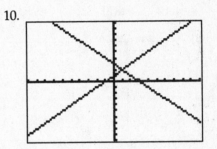

8. From a table we chose a vertical span from 0 to 1.

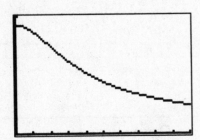

9. From a table we chose a vertical span from 0 to 1.

10.

Answers for Section 2.3

1. $x = 7$

2. $x = \dfrac{16}{3}$

3. $x = -\dfrac{20}{9}$

4. $x = \dfrac{29}{8}$

5. $x = -\dfrac{38}{43}$

6. $x = -5$

7. $x = \dfrac{12 - d}{c}$

8. $c = \dfrac{r}{c}$

9. $k = \dfrac{m - n}{3}$

10. $t = \dfrac{1}{x^2 - 1}$

Answers for Section 2.4

1. We used the standard viewing window.

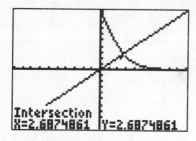

$x = 2.69$

2. We used a horizontal span of -2 to 5 and a vertical span of 0 to 5.

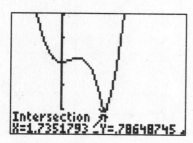

$x = 1.73$

3. We used a horizontal span of -2 to 2 and a vertical span of 0 to 5.

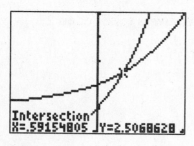

$x = 0.59$

4. We used a horizontal span of -2 to 2 and a vertical span of 0 to 5.

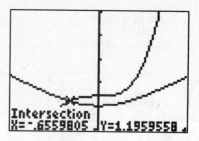

$x = -0.66$

5. For the window we use a horizontal span of -5 to 5 and a horizontal span of 0 to 7.

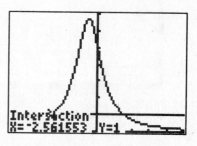

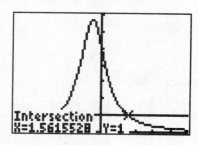

$x = -2.56$ and $x = 1.56$

6. We graph $\dfrac{20}{1 + 2^x} - x$ using the standard viewing window.

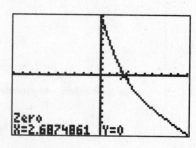

$x = 2.68$

7. We graph $\dfrac{5}{x^2 + x + 1} - 1$ using a horizontal span of -4 to 4 and a vertical span from -3 to 6.

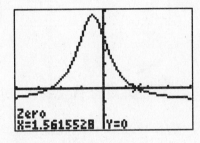

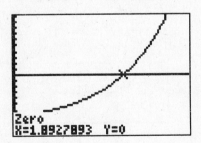

$x = -2.56$ and $x = 1.56$

8. We graph $3^x - 8$ using a horizontal span of 0 to 3 and a vertical span of -10 to 10.

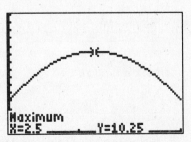

$x = 1.89$

9. We graph $\dfrac{-x^4}{x^2 + 1} + 1$ using a horizontal span of -2 to 2 and a vertical span of -2 to 2.

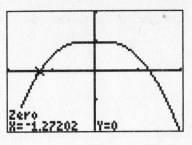

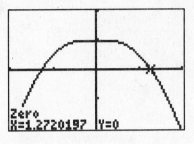

$x = -1.27$ and $x = 1.27$

10. We graph $x^3 - x - 5$ using a horizontal span of 0 to 3 and a vertical span of -10 to 10.

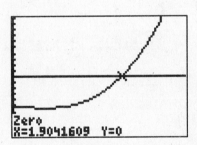

$x = 1.90$

Answers for Section 2.5

1. A table of values leads us to choose a vertical span of 0 to 15.

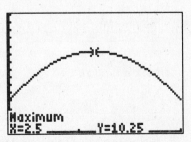

Maximum value of 10.25 at $x = 2.5$

2. A table of values leads us to choose a vertical span of 0 to 15.

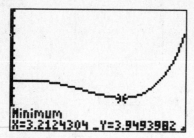

Minimum value of 3.95 at $x = 3.21$

3. A table of values leads us to choose a vertical span of 0 to 7.

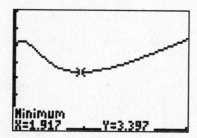

Minimum value of 3.40 at $x = 1.92$

4. A table of values leads us to choose a vertical span of -30 to 30.

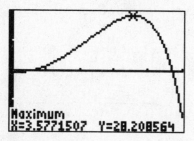

Maximum value of 28.21 at $x = 3.58$

5. We use a vertical span of 0 to 3.

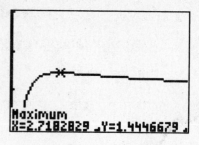

Maximum value of 1.44 at $x = 2.72$

6. We use a vertical span of 0 to 35.

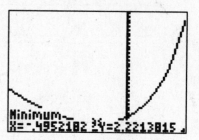

Minimum value of 2.22 at $x = -0.50$

7.

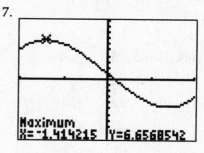

Maximum $x = -1.41$, $y = 6.66$

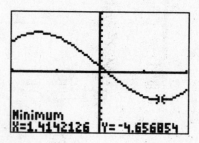

Minimum: $x = 1.41$, $y = -4.66$

8. Consulting a table of values leads us to choose a vertical span of -5 to 5.

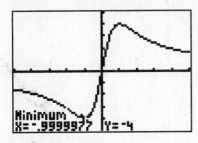

Minimum $x = -1, y = -4$

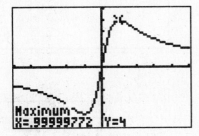

Maximum $x = 1, y = 4$

9. We use a horizontal span of 0 to 5 and a vertical span of 0 to 130. Since the graph is increasing, the maximum occurs at the end point.

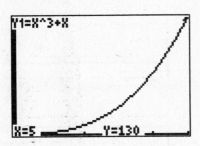

Maximum value of 130 at $x = 5$

10. We use a horizontal span of 0 to 5 and a vertical span of 0 to 200. Since the graph is decreasing, the minimum occurs at the end point.

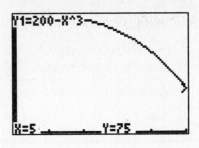

Minimum value of 75 at $x = 5$

Answers for Section 3.1

1. 4

2. 5

3. 7.5 feet

4. 6.8 feet

5. 5.14 feet

6. 5.71 feet

7. $-\dfrac{2}{3}$

8. 6.67 feet

9. 16.4 feet

10. 27.5 feet

Answers for Section 3.2

1. 4

2. -0.8

3. $f(5) = 12.4$

4. $f(12) = 23.7$

5. $x = 2.76$

6. $x = 6.15$

7. $f = 4x - 7$

8. $f = -3x + 14$

9. $f = -1.2x + 12.8$

10. $f = -2.25x + 11.75$

Answers for Section 3.3

1. There is a constant change of 2 in x and a constant change of 5 in y. The data is linear.

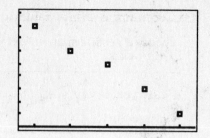

2. There is a constant change of 2 in x, but the data does not show a constant change in y. The data is not linear.

8.

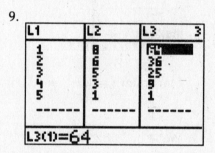

3. $y = 2.5x + 7$

4. $y = 2x + 9$

5.

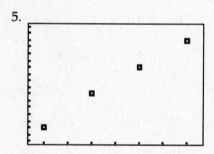

9.

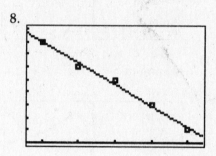

6.

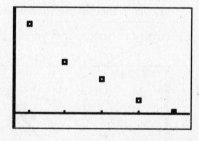

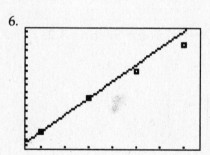

10.

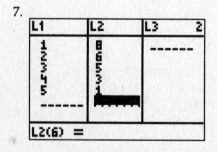

7.

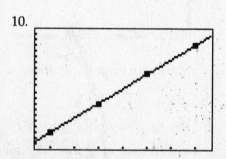

Answers for Section 3.4

1. Increasing.

2. Each year money spent on education increases by about $2300.

3. Federal spending on agriculture is increasing faster than federal spending on research and development.

4. Each additional inch in length adds about 1.38 miles per hour to the running speed.

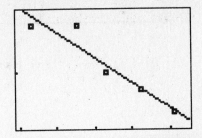

5.

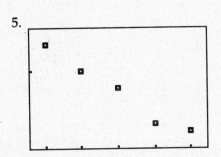

$y = -0.26x + 2.54$

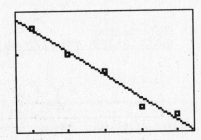

$y = -0.32x + 3.14$

6.

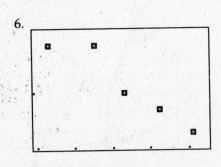

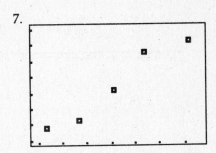

7.

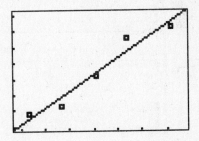

$y = 1.05x + 2.06$

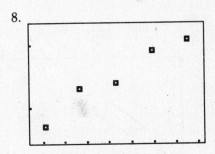

8.

$y = 0.21x + 6.93$

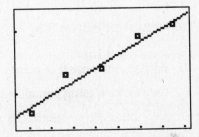

9.

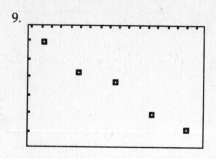

$$y = -0.32x - 1.59$$

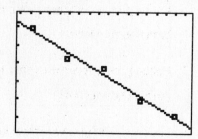

10.

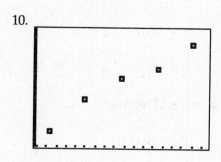

$$y = 3.09x + 3.92$$

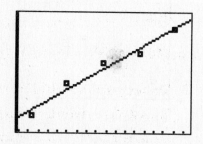

Answers for Section 3.5

1. Each graph consists of points that make the corresponding equation true. The solution of the system is the point that makes both true, and that is the common intersection point.

2. Since the graphs do not cross, there is no solution.

3. We graphed $y = \dfrac{6 - 3x}{4}$ and $y = \dfrac{5 - 2x}{-6}$ using a horizontal span of 0 to 5 and a vertical span of -3 to 3.

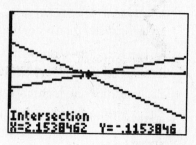

$$x = 2.15, y = -0.12$$

4. We graphed $y = \dfrac{79 + 7x}{21}$ and $\dfrac{6 - 13x}{17}$ using a horizontal span of -5 to 0 and a vertical span of 0 to 5.

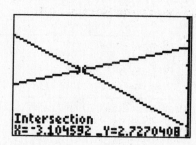

$$x = -3.10, y = 2.73$$

5. We graphed $y = \dfrac{6.6 - 0.7x}{5.3}$ and $\dfrac{1.7 - 5.2x}{2.2}$ using a horizontal span of -2 to 2 and a vertical span of 0 to 5.

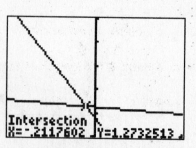

$$x = -0.21, y = 1.27$$

6. We graphed $y = \dfrac{17.1 + 6.6x}{-26.5}$ and $y = \dfrac{8.4 - 6.9x}{5.5}$ using a horizontal span of 0 to 5 and a vertical span of -2 to 2.

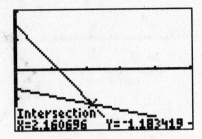

$x = 2.16, y = -1.18$

7. $x = 2.15, y = -0.12$

8. $x = -3.10, y = 2.73$

9. $x = -0.21, y = 1.27$

10. $x = 2.16, y = -1.18$

Answers for Section 4.1

1. $f(2) = 17.28$
   $f(x) = 3 \times 2.4^x$

2. $f(2) = 3.53$
   $f(x) = 400 \times 0.094^x$

3. 1.25

4. Decreasing

5. It is proportional to the function value.

6. 10×1.07^t, with t in years.

7. 10×0.96^t, with t in years.

8. Month: 1.013. Decade: 4.81.

9. 0.72%

10. 1.54%

Answers for Section 4.2

1. $N = 7 \times 8^t$

2. $N = 6 \times \left(\dfrac{1}{13}\right)^t$ or $N = 6 \times 0.077^t$

3. $N = 12 \times 1.803^t$

4. $N = 0.218 \times 1.94^t$

5. $N = 2.733 \times 1.347^t$

6. Ratios give a constant value of 3. The data is exponential.

7. Ratios give a constant value of 2. The data is exponential.

8. Ratios do not give a constant value. The data is not exponential.

9. 5×1.41^x

10. 2.6×3^x

Answers for Section 4.3

1. Exponential.

2. Linear.

3. 0.463

4. 54.60×20.09^t

5. The regression line is $0.671x + 0.798$. The alternative form for the exponential model is $2.22e^{0.671x}$. The standard form is 2.22×1.96^x.

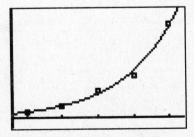

6. The regression line is $-1.029x + 0.794$. The alternative form for the exponential model is $2.21e^{-1.029x}$. The standard form is 2.21×0.36^x.

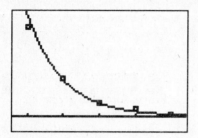

7. The regression line is $0.031x + 1.849$. The alternative form for the exponential model is $6.35e^{0.031x}$. The standard form is 6.35×1.03^x.

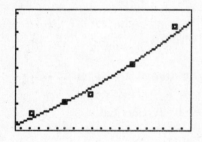

8. The regression line is $-0.206x + 1.721$. The alternative form for the exponential model is $5.59e^{-0.206x}$. The standard form is 5.59×0.81^x.

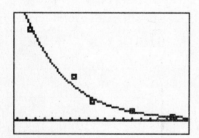

9. The regression line is $0.335x + 0.873$. The alternative form for the exponential model is $2.39e^{0.335x}$. The standard form

is 2.39×1.40^x.

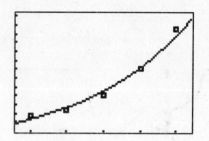

10. The regression line is $0.85x + 0.959$. The alternative form for the exponential model is $2.61e^{0.85x}$. The standard form is 2.61×2.34^x.

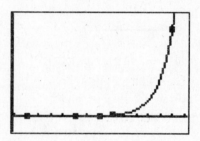

Answers for Section 4.4

1. 1.10

2. Yearly growth factor: 1.105
   EAR: 10.5%.

3. 73.7

4. $4e^{-0.26t}$

5. $5e^{1.68t}$

6. $4e^{2.26t}$

7. 7×897.85^t

8. 3×0.08^t

9. $12e^{2m}$, with m in months.

10. $12e^{36.7d}$, with d in decades.

Answers for Section 5.1

1. Decreasing.

2. Increasing.

3. 5.03

4. 1.54

5. $f(5.5)$ is 3.74 times as large as $f(3.6)$.

6. y is 2.03 times larger than z.

7. $k = 1.38$

8. $c = 0.024$

9. $c = 92.05$

10. 1.0002^x

Answers for Section 5.2

1. Linear.

2. f is a power function.
   $f = 7.39x^3$

3. 3

4. 54.60

5. Regression formula: $1.3x + 1.28$.
   Power formula: $f = 3.6x^{1.3}$.

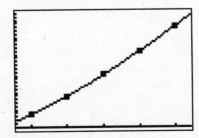

6. Regression formula: $-2.74x + 2.165$.
   Power formula: $8.71x^{-2.74}$.

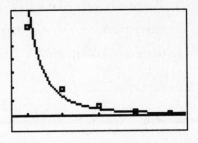

7. Regression formula: $4.54x + 0.802$.
   Power formula: $2.23x^{4.54}$.

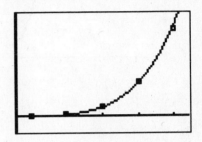

8. Regression formula: $1.73x + 1.617$.
   Power formula: $5.04x^{1.73}$.

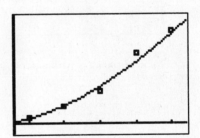

9. Regression formula: $-0.90x + 0.719$.
   Power formula: $2.05x^{-0.90}$.

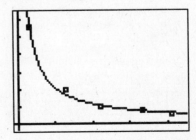

10. Regression formula: $-2.74x + 0.940$. The power formula and the plot are the same as in Exercise 6.

Answers for Section 5.3

1. $4\sin\left(\dfrac{360x}{17}\right)$

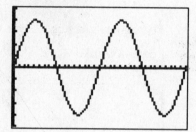

2. $3\sin\left(\dfrac{360x}{6}\right)$

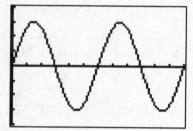

3. $\sin\theta = \dfrac{12}{13} = 0.923$
   $\cos\theta = \dfrac{5}{13} = 0.385$
   $\tan\theta = \dfrac{12}{5} = 2.4$

4. 96.16 feet

5. 24.90 feet

6. 15.72 degrees

7. 27.25 degrees

8. About 73.8 feet.

9. 133.42 feet

10. 19.28 feet

11. amplitude $= 18$
    period $= 90.45$

Answers for Section 5.4

1. It is a linear function.

2. The data shows a constant second-order difference of 4. The data is quadratic.

3. The data does not show constant second-order differences. The data is not quadratic.

4. $x = 1.43$ and $x = 0.23$

5. $x = -1.16$ and $x = 2.16$

6. $x = 1.26$ and $x = -1.26$

7. (a) is a polynomial of degree 8 and (c) is a polynomial of degree 4. The other two functions are not polynomials.

8. The nth-order differences are constant.

9. A ratio of polynomial functions.

10. $x = 1.43$ and $x = 0.23$

Answers for Section 6.1

1. Velocity.

2. Negative.
   Zero.

3. Below the horizontal axis.

4. A linear function.

5. It is a horizontal line.

6. The velocity is zero.

7. 60 miles per hour.

8. (a) Velocity is positive.

   (b) Velocity is zero.

   (c) Velocity is negative.

9. (a) Velocity is positive.

   (b) Velocity is zero.

   (c) Velocity is negative.

10. It is a horizontal line.

Answers for Section 6.2

1. (a) Velocity

   (b) Acceleration

   (c) Marginal tax rate

   (d) Marginal profit

2. The derivative.

3. (a) $\frac{df}{dx}$ is positive.

   (b) $\frac{df}{dx}$ is zero.

   (c) $\frac{df}{dx}$ is negative.

   (d) $\frac{df}{dx}$ is zero.

4. A linear function.

5. 10

6. It is positive.

7. $13.20

8. (a) The graph of $\frac{df}{dx}$ is above the horizontal axis.

   (b) The graph of $\frac{df}{dx}$ is on the horizontal axis.

   (c) The graph of $\frac{df}{dx}$ is below the horizontal axis.

   (d) The graph of $\frac{df}{dx}$ is a horizontal line.

9. The graph of f is decreasing.

10. Spend less.

Answers for Section 6.3

1. Differential equation.

2. A linear function.

3. 5

4. An exponential function.

5. $c = 8$

6. Newton's law of cooling, exponential population growth, compound interest, radioactive decay, and many others.

7. $\frac{dV}{dt} = -\frac{1}{3}V$

8. $V = 4e^{-\frac{1}{3}t}$

9. $f = 3x + 7$

10. $\frac{dv}{dt} = 32$

Answers for Section 6.4

1. A solution which does not change (remains constant).

2. 0

3. $f = 3$.

4. (a) It is negative.

   (b) It is decreasing.

   (c) It is positive.

   (d) It is increasing.

5. 15 cubic feet.

6. Decreasing.

7. Increasing.

8. 6300

9. Increasing.

10. Decreasing.

Answers for Section 6.5

1. 7

2. 2.4

3. −5.6

4. 6

5. −0.03

6. From the figure below, we get a value of 21.

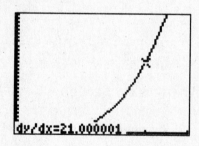

7. From the figure below, we get a value of 0.89.

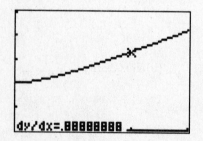

8. From the figure below, we get a value of 5.55.

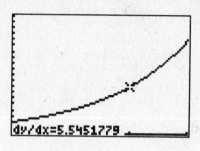

9. From the figure below, we get a value of −0.04.

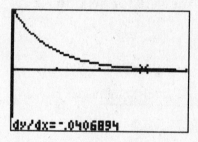

10. The rate of change is near zero.

Answers for Section 7.1

1. $\dfrac{dN}{dt} = B - D$

2. If $B = bN$ and $D = dN$, then $\dfrac{dN}{dt} = B - D = bN - dN = (b - d)N$, and $\dfrac{dN}{dt} = (b-d)N$ is the equation of change for an exponential function.

3. $\dfrac{dN}{dt} = 0.027N$

4. It is the initial value of the population.

5. r is a measure of the intrinsic per capita growth rate of a population in an environment.

6. The first population grows faster than the second.

7. It declines.

8. 0.96 year.

9. 0.05 per year.

10. Geometric growth.

Answers for Section 7.2

1. Logistic model.

2. $\dfrac{dN}{dt} = rN\left(1 - \dfrac{N}{K}\right)$

3. (a) 0.13

   (b) 378

   (c) $N = 0$ and $N = K = 378$

   (d) 189

4. Linear.

5. $N = \dfrac{K}{1 + be^{-rt}}$

6. $b = \dfrac{K}{N_0} - 1$

7. $N = \dfrac{2390}{1 + 18.92e^{-0.015t}}$

8. The maximum sustainable yield model.

9. 389

10. It is the inflection point on the logistic curve.

Answers for Section 7.3

1. A group of individuals in the same age range.

2. $x =$ age at beginning of interval

   $l_x =$ number of survivors at beginning of age interval

   $d_x =$ number dying during the age interval

   $q_x =$ proportion of individuals dying during age interval (age-specific mortality rate)

3. $q_x = \dfrac{d_x}{l_x}$.

4. $d_5 = 25$

   $q_5 = 0.083$

5. 400

6. 120

7. $q_{31} = 0.3$

   $l_{32} = 280$

8. The graph of l_x versus x, usually drawn on a semi-logarithmic scale.

9. It shows how many individuals survive to a given age.

10. All of the individuals eventually die.

Index

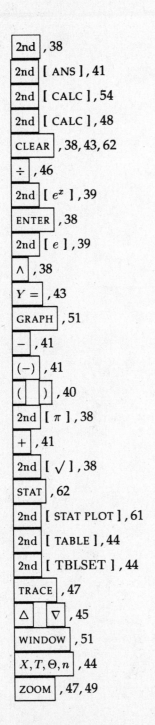